Meditative Provings

Volume 2

Notes on the Meditative Provings of New Remedies

Madeline Evans

THE ROSE
PRESS

Meditative Provings, Volume 2:

Notes on the Meditative Provings of New Remedies

1st edition, 2005

© Madeline Evans, 2005

ISBN 0-9538880-1-0

Published by	Rose Press Publications Ltd Dove House 63 Hob Moor Drive Holgate York YO24 4JU UK
Further copies from	Rose Press Publications Ltd · Dove House 63 Hob Moor Drive Holgate York YO24 4JU UK
Designed and produced by *Printed and bound by*	David Ellis Sessions of York, Huntington Road York YO31 9HS

Acknowledgements

My thanks and love go to all those who participated in the provings which produced this book. They are too numerous to mention individually, involving groups in Kent, York and Skipton. My thanks and love go to David Ellis for the typesetting and liasing with printers, and a special thank you to Peter Graves for his love and support.

About the Author

Madeline Evans has been practising Homeopathy since 1979, first in London and since 1983 in York. She founded the Yorkshire School of Homeopathy in 1984 and has taught on many under- and postgraduate courses and presented papers at the Irish and English Homeopathy Conferences. She taught at the Guild of Homeopaths and edited its journal Prometheus from 1997 until its demise in 2000. She has run courses in York for many years, combining homeopathy and spiritual development through meditation and work with the chakras. She teaches regularly on seminars.

For information on courses and seminars go to her website: www.madelineevans.com

Contents

Introduction

Introduction

The majority of the remedies for this book were proved in meditation, like those in Volume 1, by two groups of homeopaths in Kent during the 1990s. Many of them have also had additional provings by groups in York. The notes on Bog Asphodel, Butterfly, Forget-me-not, Kigelia, Nettle, Sapphire, Selenite and Slate have all come from provings in North Yorkshire alone.

I have decided to keep to the English names as people seem to prefer them to the Latin names. There has been no attempt at a repertory in this volume as a definitive repertory for the remedies in this and Volume 1 will be published shortly. I have included more information about the source of each remedy in response to feedback on Volume 1.

The Introduction for Volume 1 also relates to this volume. All the remedies were proved in a 30th potency except Milky Way for which the essence was used. Almost all were 'blind' provings - the provers knew nothing about the remedy they were taking.

As with volume 1, I have kept as much as possible of the original words of the provers in order to try to convey the spirit of the remedy more clearly. Sometimes this has meant some repetition which I have retained because I believe it enhances this spirit.

I have included a compilation of channellings on love and heart energy at the end of the book, as the opening of the Heart Chakra is of such importance at the moment. We all need reminding to keep our Hearts open and to work with love, not only with our patients but through our whole lives.

Using the Materia Medica

After the introductory section for each remedy there are either one or two common headings:

ESOTERIC

CHAKRAS

followed by a number of headings in italics which describe the major themes for the remedy, for example:

HEART, PROTECTION, FLUID

Then follows another set of common headings, although they are not all used for each remedy:

MENTAL

EMOTIONAL

GENERAL

PHYSICAL

CONNECTIONS

MIASMS

REMEDIES

PRESCRIBING NOTES

Combination remedies (often in triads) are shown as Remedy + Remedy + Remedy.

Remedy index by Latin names

The Remedies

Almond Tree Prunus dulcis

This remedy was made from nut, twig and leaf obtained from an ancient tree growing near temple ruins in Sicily. The almond is a small tree, only growing 3-12 m high. It flowers February-April, so the crop is susceptible to late frosts, even in the Mediterranean and it fruits in late summer. It is native to SW Asia but is now prolifically grown in California and southern Europe and the Mediterranean, where it is known to have been grown for at least 4,000 years. It is part of the rose family and so is also allied to the plum, pear and cherry. There are bitter and sweet varieties; the remedy is made from the sweet. The bitter contains more hydrocyanic acid and is the variety used for flavouring.

Almonds are high in monosaturated fatty acids and calcium and are the most nutritious of all nuts. They contain phytochemicals thought to prevent heart disease and cancer and rhizveritrol which is also found in red wine and protects against heart disease. It has been found to lower cholesterol in one clinical trial. Almonds, like apricot kernels, are high in vitamin B17 which is known to have anti-cancer properties. Generally people who eat more nuts do not put on weight.

Marzipan - made from ground almonds and sugar - has been associated with Easter since pre-Christian times - hence its name 'marchepain' - and so it has always been connected with rebirth, new life and regeneration. Now it is also associated with Christmas and any celebration.

Almonds are highly valued as a food, in cooking, as oil and as flavouring. The nut has been used to cure flatulence, coughing and heartburn, while the oil is well known as an emollient for softening the skin. The Chinese also used almond oil as an anaesthetic and muscle relaxant.

Bitter almonds and to lesser extent sweet, contain an oil called benzahaledyde which in the presence of water yields glucose and prussic acid (also known as hydrocyanic acid.) The cyanide produced by plants is neutralised in the stomach of most animals (including humans) except ruminants. Poisoning in humans begins with burning in the mouth, a sensation of constriction or numbness in the throat and a bitter almond odour on the breath. It progresses to irregular breathing and lack of oxygen culminating in paralysis, coma and heart failure. Death from high levels occurs within ten minutes. Cyanide is used industrially to extract gold and silver from ore.

ESOTERIC

Will bring very strong connection with the light, with the God-force. At the same time it will help maintain a very powerful connection to the Earth.

Great powers of psychic mobility in this remedy.

May have a specific three-fold activity or dimension, concerning the past, present and future, but also it is a triangular energy and that can be interpreted and used in many ways. Egyptian hieroglyphs and Hebrew characters are like that. They have three-fold meanings: a very deep spiritual meaning, a symbolic meaning and a more material meaning.

Helps to give you a special link with the spiritual father vibration. Makes you aware on a higher level of the father.

Will link you with the father/mother God and make you secure within yourselves.

Will help to reinstate the 12 strands of DNA we are said to have once had, can begin this process again. A new initiation for those who are ready.

Can lead us home and reunite with the source. Any remedy which brings such ease of connection can do this.

Has much to do with joining us all together, moving us beyond separation.

CHAKRAS

Strong connection to Upper Brow and Crown.

Very strong deep Heart connection.

Strong connection with the Brow and the Crown and the Upper Brow.

For where Crown is closed: cut off from God and any sustaining source.

SECURITY

Security is the keynote on all levels, for it brings security to the soul. And once the soul feels secure it can be at peace, understanding comes and deep trauma and old karma of huge magnitude can be released. The soul then radiates light.

The more secure you feel, the less your need to question.

Can put the patient at ease, make them feel comfortable, but secure is the keynote. In doing this, the remedy will often cushion blows, blank out without suppressing mental and emotional traumas of many blows, therefore has uses on many levels.

Almond Tree

Can make you feel secure on whatever level that security is required.

Brings stillness and peace. It slows and calms us.

Is a remedy that can bring much solace to many souls.

CHILDREN

Good for children who have lost a parent either through death or divorce, or any sort of trauma that would make them insecure i.e. changing school, moving house, etc.

For young children who suffer nightmares, vivid dreams of terrible fear, of murder. Greater ability to bring peace and healing than Stramonium, so that they do not need to transmute that karmic lesson and challenge any more.

Heals the inner child. Comfort, reliability and security. Listening to what the inner child is telling us.

Once a child becomes secure, it smiles, it radiates light.

TRAUMA AND TERROR

Great peace and healing with this remedy, particularly for groups of people.

Deep karmic healing, and healing of many traumas.

Can bring resolution, peace once more to a tortured soul.

Brings out unsuspected trauma and releases it.

Will help everyone through trauma, bring them back to base and ground them.

All cases of shock, bereavement, trauma, illness and stress.

Pain of grief and trauma locked, especially in the throat.

Brings karmic release; enables people to be free from pain, to be free to run their lives, to leave the vacuum, the trap, the restriction of sadness, pain and fear from the past.

For people who are greatly affected by the news, disaster, murder; who never feel at ease or comforted and indeed feel it is detrimental to be so.

For those who are stalwart and cut off from emotion. Detached.

Is a good remedy to keep you also in your body when states of distress occur and you need to remain in your body. Can be given before telling of bad news and can stop over-excitement from good news. Many uses in this area.

WAR AND VIOLENCE

Wars, bombs, hand battle, radiation.

The last two world wars. Heals the souls of those experiences.

For people who have dreams, nightmares, even as children, or fear of wars, of being murdered, of being killed in various scenarios, particularly where groups are involved with fear and powerlessness.

Survivors of war, and those who have ancestors, relatives killed in groups, and are still greatly touched and affected by their ancestral past.

Can be projected in various ways to help the healing of present day wars and mass killing.

Karma and trauma from lives in concentration camps.

Karmic experience where people have died in great distress. Where there has been much bloodshed, much fear and a great sense of powerlessness, of a stronger force destroying these groups of people.

Can transmute the karma from war, helps it to heal more quickly.

Those who have committed war crimes; helps to heal the karma that they have created and been involved in and helps the victims, those who hunt them down, of their pain and anger, for they in their own way, are stuck and held.

HEALING THE EARTH

Important to heal the earth of great tragedies from more recent history. Brings peace to the present day so the earth can be healed and its vibrations to move onwards and upwards.

Will bring very strong healing to the Earth, so go out and spread it on the land. You may also add it to the water supply anywhere.

Will especially help where the water is fluoridated to combat that poison.

Can be used to heal: vast graveyards from the wars; sites of concentration camps; great prisons of all sorts where there has been great terror and distress in the past.

Heals the land of the memory of fear, distress and great sadness caused by war.

BRAIN

Will block chuntering brains, nervous activity without suppressing them. Will allow a calmness and security to be felt within.

Blanks out negative brain activity and helps you to aspire to levels of the brain which are useful. For now remember new areas of the brain will be used as energy changes and some old areas are made redundant.

Lifts you up above that greyness that the brain can drop you in.

RADIATION

Excellent for protecting against and clearing radiation.

For the thyroid, parathyroid, the Throat Chakra destroyed or left wide open through radiation.

CHANGE

Those who have lost their way, who do not know where they are going any more, those who are lost and searching and feel alone.

People who need to find new meaning in their lives.

For those who have made themselves sick through over-indulgence, unhealthy pastimes, too much food, drink and drugs, too much sitting about, watching TV.

Supports the big changes in habit that are needed in order for people to become healthy.

For those who have become lethargic and irritable, too lazy to change anything. This remedy wakes them up.

For people who have decided to die before it is their time; gives them a new lease of life. Helps people to start again, be re-born in some way. Gets things moving for people.

For those who continue to make the same mistakes although they have been told.

MAGIC

Remedy is one of magic.

And it can grant all your wishes, providing they are not of a selfish nature – you use them wisely – your intention must be correct and you must never ask for selfish things. With the correct intent, this remedy can grant you three wishes.

Sense of power, of moving towards, uniting with one another in groups, that infinite energy, becoming magicians.

DEATH

Another excellent remedy to use for the dying and also to place in hospices, for it will make the soul feel secure in its new state of being.

It will help to cleanse a hospice, to move souls on that are stuck. Would be useful with Rainbow, for the transition.

Helps those those around the dying - for grief.

Helps those dying young leave the worry for those they leave behind.

For the dying and the pathology of death. Helps the pain of malignancies and eases the pain of physical body shutting down as death approaches.

Has a great ability to dredge up many souls who have remained earthbound and stuck in the darkness and terror of confusion through passing over from great destruction and particularly of souls who have died from radiation in one form or another.

CANCER

Terminal cancer patients and for all cancers, for will bring understanding to the soul, acknowledgement of their denial and their fear and in some cases may be very curative indeed.

Eases cancer states on every level, releases miasm and prevents cancer being taken forward to next life.

For those who are spiritually evolved who develop cancer.

Will help the souls who have elected to die of cancer. Will help them to have understanding of their acknowledgement of themselves, their karma and their condition. Will help them to open.

Will have most therapeutic use in pathology of cancer, for may be one of your new remedies of biggest help in all cases of carcinoma with suppressed and malignant states of mind.

It may not cure the carcinogenic state but it will help greatly the state of mind.

Cancer of the pituitary. Also endocrine cancers, particularly reproductive system - breast, ovaries, uterus and testes.

JOINTS

For all malignant states in the joints. Where chuntering negativities in the mind have caused the liver energy to become negative and negative energy has poured into the joints from generation to generation. As security and peace comes to the soul, into the heart, these states can be purified.

Almond Tree

Useful for rheumatoid and osteoarthritis, joint pains, for all destructive states of the joints. Will help relieve pain and assist in healing fractures.

For bitter and twisted states of mind where the joints finally crumble as a result of negative liver activity.

GENERAL

Is good for all malignant states of body, mind and soul.

Stuck states and stuck energy. Attitudes stuck through fear.

Blocks that are hard to shift and for the trauma behind these blocks.

Many therapeutic uses.

States of stagnation, stasis, congestion, weakness. Everything is dying inside. Things seizing up, blood vessels, muscles wasting; internal organs not being used properly.

Circulation.

Ulceration, sepsis.

Sensation of being split and R side larger.

Numbness R side.

Helpful for sleep problems, for it puts one at ease.

Connection with blood and circulation.

Major remedy for travel at speed and for jetlag.

PHYSICAL

Head: L sided headache. Sinus pain L teeth. Strong connection with the pituitary gland. Sensation as if I wanted to take my head off to relieve such a heavy weight.

Sensations up in Crown area on L side.

Eyes: helps with hearing and sight problems, physically and on all levels.

Ears: strong link to the ears, hearing. Hearing impaired through nerve damage. Can achieve the impossible in improving hearing.

Tinnitus.

Throat: nausea in the solar plexus and throat areas.

Numbness of the throat, tongue, soft palate.

Abdomen: sensation of tight stretched abdomen, like a drum.

Back: pain from under L shoulder blade to L breast. Burning pains in back.

Extremities: numbness L foot. Hands felt as if in stinging nettles.

Aware of the two clavicles and where they join. Soreness, not on the joint, on the length of the bones, especially L side.

Pain in L knee as if nail driven in.

Pain R shoulder.

Female: P.M.T. Could have murdered someone. Wanting to be alone – had enough. Weepy, oversympathetic.

People who are trying to conceive. Helps remove blocks and can even help the incoming soul.

CONNECTIONS

With royalty.

With the fragility and beauty and refined energy around the birth of a baby.

With the power of music or sound.

A pyramid made of lines that could be seen through.

The word Chaldean.

MIASMS

Radiation miasm.

Cancer miasm.

REMEDIES

Excellent used with all polychrests, for will help them to work at much deeper level.

Pulsatilla. Tuberculinum. Lotus. Gorse. Arsenicum.

Rainbow should sometimes be given before.

Give before Buddleia, Lotus and other trauma remedies.

Remedy has very noble quality, superior like Platina in a negative sense and the positive qualities of refinement.

Forms triangle with Thuja and Calc Carb, so is close to both. The three together grant your wishes. These three remedies either in combination or parallel restart the spinning of the chakras the correct way and somehow that is connected with the security.

Almond Tree

PRESCRIBING NOTES

Remedy is one of great power. Should be given to absolutely everyone.

Works slowly at a deep level.

Good in high potency. Best given in higher potencies.

Very repeatable at 30C potency during pregnancy and can be repeated 3 times weekly to ensure security of incoming soul. If mother suffers with much insecurity, it can be repeated daily for first three months. Brings much peace and quiet. You will watch the soul shine.

Important for old people.

Ametrine

T his crystal is a mixture of amethyst and citrine and so it combines the properties of both of these crystals and the colours of purple and yellow. Both are varieties of quartz crystal which were said to be in the breastplate of the High Priest in Jerusalem. The citrine enables a dissipation and transmutation of negative energy while the amethyst raises the vibration and is a stone of transformation, also producing calmness and relaxation. Both link the Base and Crown chakras and stimulate the movement of energy along the spine.

Ametrine is a crystal which links heaven and earth, spirit and matter. In meditation it stimulates you to reach beyond the mundane and into the higher realms and it can enhance meditation by helping you to reach higher levels of consciousness. It removes negative vibration from the aura and releases blockages in the physical, emotional and mental bodies bringing relaxation, peace and tranquility. It links the lower and higher aspects of the mind, the intellect with the heart and allows the release of judgement and prejudice. It helps to produce equilibrium of all the subtle bodies and releases negative programming from the emotional body. It is a stone of majesty and power, but at the same time is gentle and friendly.

ESOTERIC
For the abuse of Kundalini energy in the past, which has damaged the nervous system. For the damaged blueprint held in the Thymus.

CHAKRAS
Affects Crown, Base, Heart, Brow, all the head centres and the pituitary. Throat and Thymus. Crown and Base.

TRANSFORMATION
Awakening, transformation, cutting away the old and releasing the new. Breaking down rigidity. Structures breaking down and being broken down where needed.

Images of transformation: frogs; snake; spring.

Transformational states: menopause, pregnancy, death.

People who find the changes hard and do not know why - because of old grief in the Thymus.

Ametrine

NERVOUS SYSTEM & HEAD

Repairs cells, heals the brain and nervous system. A remedy that can really get into every area of the brain.

Head injuries. Brain damage. Communication affected and the nervous system.

Memory loss following war and violence.

Pressure at the back of the neck up into the back of the head like a blow.

Tingling then heat across the crown, spreading down the back of the head.

A sense of smallness and deformity around the forehead.

Hyperactivity, with confusion in head; emotionally not knowing how to deal with it.

Feeling crushed. Brain fag, burn out.

MS. Cerebral palsy. Motor neurone disease. Spina bifida. Stroke. Accident. Aphasia. Birth that has damaged the skull. Cleft palate. Acromegaly. Shingles.

EMOTIONAL

Hidden trauma and abuse.

A lot of pain in held in the throat and thymus. Tremendous grief and pain locked in the throat especially from sexual abuse.

Sense of isolation. For the despair of not being able to make the body do what you want it to do - the remedy will help with acceptance. For feeling overwhelmed by the task and not knowing what you are coping with never mind how.

A sense of unworthiness - don't deserve the light

Fear of malformation of baby in pregnancy.

For the trauma following war and violent conflict. Post-war stress: for those having difficulty surviving. Good for the mental, emotional and physical problems from the trauma of violence.

Trauma from injuries with knives. Self harm and cutting oneself.

GENERAL

Sense of deep dark stuff.

Burning.

R sided.

Tingling.
Sensations of contraction and diminution.

PHYSICAL
Throat: catarrh, needing to clear throat. Soreness L to R. Throat hurts talking.
Eyes: blurring and clearing - like cataracts. Soreness around both eyes; hot and watery eyes.
Nose: twitching.
Ears: ringing.
Neck: tension, as if neck being pulled.
Joints: arthritic and rheumatic.
Bones: fractures, osteoporosis.
Extremities: a lot of tingling on the bottom of the feet and hands.

MIASMS
A very syphilitic remedy. All hidden. Nobody knows it is there.

CONNECTIONS
With war: civil war, fighting in cities, neighbour fighting neighbour, people fighting who were once friends, e.g. in Bosnia, Northern Ireland, Israel and Palestine.
Knives.

REMEDIES
Oak. Sea Holly. Silver Birch. Gelsemium. A new Syphilinum. Thymus Gland.
Ametrine could be the mineral analogue of Sea Holly.

Apple Tree Malus sylvestris

The myths and symbols relating to the apple tree go back as far as Babylon and run through Hebrew, Pagan, Greek, Celtic and Christian legends. Throughout the world the apple has been connected with love and the goddesses of love. In Greek Myth the apple was Gaia's wedding gift to Hera on her marriage to Zeus. It was planted in the sacred garden on the slopes of Mount Atlas, which became the apple orchards of Paradise known as the Garden of the Hesperides after the nine maidens dedicated to looking after it. (Hesperus was Venus, the planet dedicated to Aphrodite). Paris was given a golden apple by Zeus to present to the most beautiful of the goddesses to stop them arguing. He awarded it to Aphrodite who promised him Helen of Troy; the miffed losers caused the Trojan wars as a result. The apple afterwards became known as a symbol of beauty, love and wisdom, containing Aphrodite's five-pointed star at its core when sliced across.

Hera caused a snake to be put around the roots of the sacred apple tree to stop the apples being stolen. In many of the myths of the sacred apple tree going back to Assyria and Babylon there is also a serpent or a dragon coiled round the tree to guard it. It was one of Hercules' labours to fetch an apple from this guarded tree, which he did with the help of Prometheus (the bringer of the fire of the gods to humanity and some myths say the creator of humanity). The Labours of Hercules themselves are symbolic of the soul's development and of the lessons of the zodiac. The Atlantis of Greek myth was said to be famous for its apple bearing trees. Medieval alchemists sometimes called the Philosophers' Stone 'the golden apple of Hesperides' because it provided immortality as well as turning base metal to gold.

In Western legend the apple orchards of Paradise were known as the 'Isle of the Blessed' where grew the Tree of Knowledge on which were found three sacred apples, guarded by Cerridwen in the form of a serpent. In Druidic lore the essence of these apples was formed from three drops which had escaped from Cerridwen's cauldron and which had originally descended from heaven. They corresponded to the three rays of Light, the Awen, which express the Creator. The apple tree was also special to Druids as it carried the sacred mistletoe.

In Northern Europe the apple was sacred to the goddess Iunna and conveyed immortality - the attribute of the Tree of Life in the Garden of Eden. The apple is also associated with the fairy kingdom, fertility and the birth of special human beings. The Avalon of Arthurian legend is described as the 'isle of apples' to which Arthur is taken by three fairy queens. In an

Irish legend, Prince Connla is given an apple by a beautiful fairy woman. Although he eats it, it never gets any smaller. Eventually he needs no other sustenance and one day he goes in a glass boat to the fairy kingdom where he becomes immortal.

And so there are many myths of the apple tree predating the Garden of Eden. Genesis does not state specifically that an apple was the fruit of the Tree of Good and Evil which Adam and Eve ate, but popular tradition believes it was. Here the fruit gives self awareness - a God-like quality - but the myth is changed to suit a monotheistic, patriarchal society and eating of the fruit brings, on the surface at least, a curse not a blessing. It also represents the integration of the soul into the physical body.

Apples are a universal symbol of plenty, often linked to good health and longevity. Apple trees used to be planted close to houses to ensure love in the home and to protect against lightning which is said never to strike them.

ESOTERIC

Healing power on many levels. Heals the auric shell.

The aura of the remedy is green and remedy will heal deep levels of this colour vibration. There is much delicacy in its vibration.

Has very magical quality to it and much wisdom; wisdom as opposed to clever brains.

New beginnings. Removes the fear that accompanies initiation into a new level of consciousness. Gives safety and protection in which new initiations can be undertaken.

Helps us to experience who we really are and our true mission.

Will heal nature and nature spirits. Links us with them.

Gives great comfort and succour to all who are needy. Opens them to experience Christ's love in their hearts for those who can experience its energy and power now, it opens and refines higher centres and brings them into greater affinity.

For those who already have the heart open this remedy will work with great profundity.

It symbolises the Tree of Life, all that is, was and ever shall be.

It links you back to the state of being before the Fall and takes you back to your contact with the One, with God.

Helps to align the spiritual with the physical where there is great disorder in life because the physical body is not doing what the spirit wants it to do.

Of profound importance for the New Age. It brings with it a liberation from the distant past and links you into the far future.

Its energy takes you back to the beginning of time.

Removes layers of the past and brings in layers of the future.

Will bring back to life those who are close to death, help them to see life again or to pass into the spirit world more easily.

CHAKRAS

It facilitates the opening and awakening of three new Centres; can link into parts of the being not accessed before.

Enhances flow between the chakras. Stimulates the higher Centres.

Opens the Heart and the Upper Heart. Strengthens the Heart which helps to unblock the Solar Plexus.

Of profound importance for the Crown and the Brow. Clarifies inner vision.

Grounds, especially those too busy.

Blockage in Sacral Centre with congestion in the physical organs

SENSITIVITY

Extreme sensitivity on all levels and can heal over-sensitivity wherever it may lie. Spiritual over-sensitivity which gives the individual the inclination to receive the wrong messages; mental over-sensitivity which can lead to hysteria and physical over-sensitivity which can lead to allergies in many forms. Remedy will balance out these sensitivities.

Excellent remedy for individuals who are too sensitive to live in the world, those who are frightened to be here, remedy will calm down their fear and help them to adjust.

Too sensitive to impressions.

Sensitivity can cause withdrawal so they appear dull, stupid and locked away, unresponsive, slow with little comprehension, but inside have a soul of great sensitivity and cannot deal with material world, so hide.

For souls still raw and wet who have yet to develop a protective skin.

Helps those who yearn to evolve but suffer from over-sensitivity.

Neurosis, from or with hypersensitivity.

People who are too sensitive and so they float off.

For people, especially children, whose bodies are simply not strong enough to carry the soul.

CHILDREN

Is excellent remedy for all your little ones. They will shine under its power. They are all so lost and frightened.

Especially important for young children who are afraid of school, even more so after onslaught of inoculation which damages their sensitivity even more.

A remedy of profound transformation especially for children. Many people now are too blunt to feel its power, too gross, too material - this is why for now it works so well for children but in the future all will be able to experience this remedy.

Enables children who are fearful to feel safe. Brings sleep to troubled children allowing them to turn off their fears.

Useful for children who seem scattered and fey, slight, almost not here, it will help ground them.

For relief of a child's pain - punishment, being rapped on the knuckles - a child takes that to heart and suffers in silence.

Children who are blocked off from joy.

Vaccine damaged children. Too sensitive to be here, so they opt out, go to sleep, will not learn, won't be here.

Children who appear brain damaged, stupid, but inside very sensitive souls and very close to God.

Can bring out the childlike quality in adults.

TRAUMA

For those individuals whose auras are shattered from traumatic experience in this life or past lives. Remedy will heal the aura gently and slowly repair damage like a spider weaving an intricate web.

Those who have been shocked out of their bodies by trauma, grief, vaccination, operations, anaesthetic. Any trauma or shock. Post traumatic stress disorder. It will be very important in the future.

Trauma to the Heart Centre, Thymus and Throat; trauma locked anywhere including the Brow.

People who have gone through great, great shock and have no understanding of what has happened.

Those souls who have chosen to be brain damaged from birth, birth trauma.

Apple Tree

STASIS

Re-awakes energies of many organs affected by stasis of the blood.

Has many areas of purification, for as the purification of the blood awakens, the vital force begins to shine.

Remedy purifies the digestion and the chemistry of the blood. Blood that is static with no life force, this will revitalise its spirit and bring the individual to life.

Purifies the liver and especially has a very profound effect on spleen energy. Is almost specific for revitalising stasis of blood in this area and as this energy awakens, the spirit will shine through.

Will also aid in constipation where there is stasis of the bowel.

Excellent remedy for those suffering with emphysema, stasis in the lungs.

MENTAL

A remedy for stilling the mind.

Remedy of focus - mental and visual.

Mental oppression. Will bring clarity to foggy minds. It will help people see what really matters, let go of the trivia which has been bogging them down.

EMOTIONAL

It will help the patient reveal what you need to know - particularly children and teenagers; (not willful deception); it will enable them to say what is important.

Seeks to reveal that which is in the shadow, repressed side of people's nature. Helps people come to terms with that and accept it.

Dispels anxiety from the solar plexus and heals anxiety and guilt.

It can restore joy to life, a sense of meaning when there had been despair.

It brings a sense of freedom and expansiveness where there has been constriction and tunnel vision.

GENERAL

Deep acting.

For travellers: jet lag, motion sickness, those who are travelling long distances, far from their roots. This remedy will help them be in the present. Help the physical body adjust to the time changes and keep the mind awake and alert.

Brings a sense of being sheltered and protected. A very protective remedy. Protects from negative influences.

It will restore order from chaos; physical chaos caused by drugs or mental chaos.

Mumps remedy. Mumps component of MMR vaccination. (Earthworm for measles/polio component).

Good remedy for fever e.g. glandular fever or parotid glands. Glands generally are affected.

Left sided.

Weakness, torpor, can't be bothered and want life to be over with because it's too much effort.

Slowness.

Very cold.

PHYSICAL

Head: clears headaches from mental strain.

L sided sinuses. Headaches and ear pain on L. Pain around base of neck.

Eyes: foggy vision, cataracts and everything which disturbs focus. Fatigue of the eyes with watering. Blurred vision.

Face: a peculiar sensation of skin on face being pulled up, more right sided. Heat in.

Throat: blockage; sensation of lump. Fear of choking.

Heart: blockages in heart, karmic blockages for many generations ago.

Digestive: will refine the chemistry and aid greatly in the digestive process which is so much abused on your level at the present time. Soothes and aids the mucous membrane surfaces in the alimentary canal, facilitating better and easier assimilation of food.

Abdomen: IBS - people feel pressured, stressed, confined in what they are doing. It will help them release and relax.

Kidneys: affinity for the water balance: oedema especially when the swelling is in the ankles and the feet, from heat. Urge to urinate.

Female: encourages ovulation when L ovary malfunctioning.

Nausea in pregnancy which persists beyond the 3rd month.

Where the mother feels she doesn't belong either in the culture or the country and she is unsure of her pregnancy. It will help the mother to assimilate the changes in her life.

It is useful in maintaining pregnancy where there is a history of miscarriages without reason.

Male: infertility, low sperm count or lacking in quality.

Sex: sexual energy ++. Sexual dreams. Suppressed sexuality at the base and sacral centres: from abuse, suppressed fear, guilt, inability to use sexual energy in the right way.

Extremities: tension in legs; can't relax, restless legs, twitching and jerking. Ache in L scapula. Lower back ache.

Nerves: cramping with congestive heart attack and stomach cramping especially with nerves.

REMEDIES

Works well with Silver Birch to heal the earth. Has powerful effect on earth's energies and in areas of darkness can bring light. This remedy can even disperse forces of dark magic. It brings in the earth's spirits which can heal these areas. In all areas of darkness elemental spirits are absent and remedy will bring them back.

Would work well with Sandalwood and complement many new remedies and polychrests.

Works with Silica especially also Pulsatilla, Baryta Carb, Red, all tree remedies, Sequoia and Amber.

Similar to Oak, Bellis Perennis.

PRESCRIBING NOTES

Can be used with Lotus in Baptismal front for it will bring Christ contact to the tiny being.

Can be given to all children in combination with their constitutional remedy to promote contact with the etheric world - devic and fairy kingdoms and earth energy.

Ash Tree Fraxinus excelsior

The Ash is one of Britain's most common native trees, favouring limestone areas and even growing on limestone pavements. While the crown is not so dense that plants cannot grow beneath it, the roots are acidic which discourage the growth of other plants. The timber burns even when green and freshly cut and has been traditionally used for making the handles of tools and the shafts of weapons, as it combines strength with elasticity and so resists shock. It was also coppiced for use as poles and although it is unsuitable for posts as the timber rots quickly underground, it was the traditional wood used for the maypole.

It is one of the last trees to come into leaf and an old saying uses the Ash and Oak trees as weather predictors: 'Oak before Ash, we're in for a splash. Ash before Oak, we're in for a soak.' (Its other connection with Oak is that both of them attract lightning.) The leaves fall early in autumn while still green, usually with the first cold wind or frost. The flowers are bisexual, male and female parts being borne together, but all the flowers on a single tree can be the same sex and this can vary from year to year. The seeds hanging in their easily recognised bunches of 'keys' germinate easily and are regarded as a nuisance by gardeners and foresters. Each seed has a slight twist in it to help it to spin further away from the parent tree. The keys stay on the tree well into the winter and are a useful food for birds. Although it grows rapidly and to a height of about 45 metres, it is 40 years before it produces seeds. It is deep rooted and so resilient to storms and drought. It has rarely been used as a boundary tree as it lacks a distinctive outline in winter and character in summer.

It was regarded as a healing tree in Britain until well into the eighteenth century. It was particularly used to treat children - the most common ailments being ruptures and hernias: a young, growing ash was split and the naked child passed through the split which was then bound back together. As the tree healed, so did the child. Newborn children were given the juice from an ash stick to protect them from harm. The bark was used to treat intermittent fevers, arthritis and liver disorders. The dried, powdered leaves have also been used to treat rheumatism and constipation and the tree generally used to clear warts (which were thought to be the result of a spell). The seeds were believed to have aphrodisiac properties - to 'provoke lust and make men more spirited with the ladies.'

It is common in northern European myths for humanity to have had its origins in the ash tree. The most famous myth is that of Yggdrasil, the

Ash Tree

Nordic *Tree of Life*, a huge ash tree which reached from heaven to hell, bridging the gods, the living and the dead. Odin hung himself from this tree in order to receive illumination in the form of knowledge of the runes.

In Greek mythology, Nemesis, the Greek goddess of fate, carried a rod of ash with which to implement the justice of the gods. The ash tree was regarded as one of the guises of the goddess in ancient Europe and features in many myths. It was only later that it became a symbol of the power of the sun god and masculine energy. It is linked to the water element and summer.

For the druids, the Ash was linked ceremonially with the Oak and also the Hawthorn. The Oak gave initiation to the Grove while the Ash gave protection and enabled a safe return to 'normality'. Ceremonially, the Hawthorn balanced the male energy of the Oak with its female energy while the Ash balanced the two and gave clarity of vision and direction. The druidic wand was made of ash, magical human images were carved from ash root and the wassailing bowl was carved from ash wood. Crosses with arms of equal length made of ash were carried by sailors for protection.

ESOTERIC

This is remedy from which every individual on your plane of consciousness will benefit greatly as we enter the New Age. It is an Aquarian remedy par excellence. It brings calm and much harmony into the being, enables you to feel at peace with yourselves.

It has a vibration that will come easier in time to come. Almost a remedy we are not quite ready for.

It will be one of the most powerful new polychrest remedies.

It is one of the most powerful remedies we have been given so far.

It is a promise for mankind that all mankind can receive the Christ spirit and will.

It raises the vibration of and harmonises the body so it can withstand the power of the light.

The remedy allows spirit to integrate into matter with safety. Please use this remedy well, for it has great power.

It opens the door between the conscious and the subconscious and therefore creates harmony, for it helps you to understand your mission. Calm and resignation and fills your being with light.

It allows the genetic blueprint to be understood and released thus releasing ancestral forces easily. It lightens the burden and the load.

It enhances intuition, correct intuition, for will keep away all forces which will try to impair correct intuition.

It brings harmony by balancing Yin and Yang tendencies within the psyche. It enables you to feel balanced.

It is a remedy of magic, regeneration and stability.

It opens possibilities of spiritual growth - it can breakdown structures on a physical level, structures of the past.

For those with handicap or mutation: it enables them to transmute their karma more quickly, with greater consciousness, to accept their condition, to have greater clarity and understanding even though this could be through death.

It brings great connection with the guides and spiritual beings on a high level.

It works best during the summer months, a time that is open and brings to light that which has been hidden to purify. During winter months it works like magic on those hidden ancestral energies which burden us, make our load feel heavy. If given in winter, you will see its effect in the summer; it will not be as obvious how it is working.

It works well with power of the sun: its masculine force brings stability and majesty.

CHAKRAS

It has the potential to bring enlightenment and spiritual freedom, to open the higher chakras.

Opens the Heart and Upper Heart, raises the vibration of all subtle bodies, brings refinement. Focus on the transformation between the Solar Plexus and the Heart.

It is a very strong Heart-centred remedy.

Affects the Throat.

CLEARING

Very powerful remedy for possession and will make the clearing process easier and demons release much easier. Very deep, old ancestral evil can be cleared away with this.

Allows light to permeate into every part of the being, so you must be ready for the dark places it illuminates.

Can help clear areas where there is negative vibration and dark entities that have lingered long in houses or places, particularly in places of worship.

Ash Tree

The remedy has the ability to disintegrate, to purify, so be careful with it.

A remedy for transformation of states, to rid the desire body of passion.

Very powerful light, powerfully healing. It has the ability to penetrate, purify and restructure and regenerate all levels of our being.

Can unlock things for those who have reincarnated especially to deal with an old issue.

Frees those who are stuck.

RIGIDITY

It makes the being more flexible and understanding, for rigidity is based upon fear.

Fear of letting others be who they are. Allows the person with fixed ideas to let people be as God wants them to be.

Allows flexibility of the spirit and body. Takes away fixed ideas. Allows open-mindedness. All physical states of rigidity can be helped by this remedy - rigidity of the skeletal system, rigidity of the pancreas and spleen energy.

It greatly assists fluidity. Allows the energies to flow.

Helps people to make new beginnings.

Helps people to face a change they see as difficult and about which they have great fear. Gives the ability to break through restriction and limitation.

SPLIT

Works on dual states of mind and mental symptoms almost identical to those of Thuja and Anacardium where there is division of consciousness due to the spirit not wishing to incarnate properly on higher levels of consciousness, therefore there is a fight between two sides, there is a split. It will heal the split in consciousness and bring the being into incarnation. As this happens fear and anger will dissolve.

For fragmentations in any sort of lines: etheric lines, lines of energy, of fluid.

For breaks that go deeply back into the past and are carried in our DNA. There is a spiral quality to the remedy and it has profound effect our DNA.

CHILDREN

Children will benefit greatly from its power.

It works well on children in every way.

It is probably already and will be one of best remedies to give to to children, for it lightens their spirit and their load, helps them to detach from the heavy karma of their parents and heavy vacccination load and see their way forward.

These children are sparks of light and must be purified from this damage in order to move into Aquarius for they are the lights of the future.

A good remedy to give to children generally, almost routinely, like you might give Tuberculinum. Will help them to reach their full potential on all levels, make them more rounded.

Backward and wayward teenagers and children.

DEATH

For souls approaching death who are fearful of dying and restricted in the body due to disease.

Those who are cremated before they are ready and before the etheric bodies have left the human bodies fully, the remedy will help souls to detach properly and enable them to go on into heaven. (The remedy can be taken by a relative or sent to the soul through prayer. Ed.)

Grief over loss when someone has died.

Where the soul who has passed over is clinging to relatives on earth.

REGENERATION

It brings life into the cells.

It can also which can bring life to every plant, plants which are dying, vegetation which has become sad and blocked.

SLEEP

Remedy enhances sleep by relaxing the conscious and subconscious mind. Gives a peaceful sleep with true rest to the inner worlds. Especially good for those whose aggravation time is on waking. They have not had restful sleep.

Insomnia, especially for people who cannot sleep because their lives seem to be in such a mess they cannot find or see any way out.

Sleep and the Sacral Centre.

Ash Tree

MENTAL

Improves memory. Will help us to remember a lot from the past, but it is in connection with magic and folklore, what we once knew.

Takes away cluttered thoughts, chuntering states of mind and anxieties.

EMOTIONAL

Unlocks doors, especially emotional doors, which have been shut for aeons.

For fear of the unfamiliar.

For those experiencing nervous breakdown who feel the need for self preservation.

Depression: resignation, feeling bogged down. Sense of futility, with no end in sight. They desire oblivion. Fed up, bored, great frustration. Weariness of being in this state before, many times.

Distress and grief and tears. Blocked grief. Can release anger.

Aimless children and adults who are bored all the time.

Lack of self worth, lack of capability.

Longings, yearnings and desires, yet there is great peace and tranquillity at the Heart Centre.

Brings subconscious understanding into consciousness, therefore helps to soothe, calm and ground the individual.

GENERAL

It is a powerful remedy for all on your plane of consciousness, humans, animals and plants.

It gives a perfect balance of masculine and feminine energy.

It creates a balance between breaking down and regenerating.

Gives resolution. Purity. Ash will help to clarify and clear and make the individual more responsible.

A very quiet remedy with enormous hidden strength.

Can be given to pregnant women to help the incarnating soul.

For old people, particularly when they go into a state of half dream when only their body is here in this world, the rest of them is somewhere else.

Genetic mutation and interference: past and future.

Anti-tumour qualities: breast tumours and also for nodules and tumours of the throat.

It can breakdown viruses, neoplasms and micro-organisms of all kinds.

On a cellular level it is able to break down the structures to purify and regenerate.

Slow growth.

Stiffness all over

PHYSICAL

Head: burning sensation in the head. Head irritating and itchy.
Poor brain development.

Eyes: burning, stinging and watering. Sticky thick discharge in both eyes. Watery L eye.

Nose: streaming, hayfever-type symptoms in nose. Difficult to breathe and swallow.

Neck: stiff, unable to move.

Throat: sore throat. Glandular swellings in throat.

Lungs: too hot, cannot breathe, no air. Asthma and emphysema, poor oxygenation, air hunger, poor use of iron in the body. TB constitution.
Releases tensions in diaphragm caused by emotions.

Stomach: a lot of burping.

Abdomen: helps balance pancreas and other organs.

Spleen: balances spleen energy so correct transmutation of solar energy can occur; relieves chronic fatigue or immune compromised conditions. Sense of discomfort around the solar plexus.

Urinary: allows the water balance within the body to flow correctly.

Lymph: allows lymph drainage to flow. Clears lymph nodes which have been blocked for many years. Lymph cleanser and drainer. Lymph nodules and infections.

Sacrum: aching in sacral area.

Spine: stitches in spine, almost pulsating.

Nerves: affects nerve ganglions and the nervous system structures.
For nervous disorders with jerking and choreic movements, where the soul wants to leave the body but its mission is to stay in it.
Deep nervous trouble. Paralysis. MS. Twitching, jerkings, difficulty in walking or moving.

Circulation: vein problems; for tortuous twisted veins.

Ash Tree

CONNECTIONS
With the number 13.

MIASMS
Will cut through miasmic blocks without the use of specific nosodes.

It can modify the effects of the past so it can modify and purify every miasm, every disease of which we carry the memory and after effect.

REMEDIES
A very important balancing part of any trilogy of remedies for it will maintain equilibrium and balance to allow the remedies to work without aggravation on any level of consciousness.

It enhances the effect of all sound remedies and again makes them become stronger in time so that instead of maintaining or losing their energy, their power becomes greater. It will work in similar way with colour remedies.

There is a strong connection with Oak. It follows Oak well in bringing people into consciousness and works especially well if used with Oak in a trilogy.

Combination of this remedy and Holly (best in winter) plus Oak as well would help people's consciousness to link in with the seasons and the understanding of that process within themselves in terms of cycles and activity and rest and consciousness and thought and meditation and so on.

Related to Walnut in connection with sleep, the brain, the intuition and intellect and miasmatic tendencies, creating balance between them.

Hawthorn.

It works works well with Thuja and Anacardium.

Like Berlin Wall in lack of motivation, so stuck.

It reverberates quite deeply with Buddleia and Sandalwood because they all in different ways create a space where trauma can be healed, and this one very powerfully.

PRESCRIBING NOTES
Use with Ceanothus as a low x potency or tincture where spleen energy poor, with general exhaustion and depleted energy.

Useful for those taking drugs that take them off our plane of
consciousness for sleep reasons and depressive reasons. Use Ash + Thuja
+ one other to drain spirit of such toxicity. For so many souls now so
distraught they cannot live without drugs to help, but they are not
incarnate. Probably therefore cannot fulfill their karma and many,
many possessions due to this on your level, confusing issues more.

Banyan Tree   Ficus benghalensis

The Banyan is a member of the Moraceae or mulberry family of trees of the genus Ficus or fig. It is native to India and Southeast Asia, growing in monsoon and rain forests and has been planted throughout the forest tract of India for soil conservation. It has been traditionally planted in the gardens around Hindu temples. It is a hardy, evergreen, drought resistant tree which withstands mild frost and grows quickly to a height of 100 feet. It has large oval leaves which are downy when young and small round fruit the size of a cherry, also downy, which is used to make a sherbet.

The tree spreads laterally over an enormous area, its roots spreading sideways out and sending up shoots which become new trunks. Its branches send out aerial roots and more new trunks, all of which creates the impression of many different trees growing close together, although in reality there is only one. The tree can be vast: one in Poona, India has a circumference of over half a mile, while in the Calcutta Botanical Garden, there is a single tree planted in 1787 that now spans three acres in a tangle of branches, roots, and intertwined trunks, the largest known Banyan in the world. Banyans provide cool shade and shelter and so are a habitat for a wide variety of animals and insects. They have also been widely used by people as meeting places and even for living in. Indian holy men traditionally live in Banyan trees. They were widely planted along roads in towns and cities in India and Pakistan for their shade, but there are very few now due to the pressure of people and traffic.

According to Ayurvedic medicine, Banyan is astringent to the bowels and is useful in the treatment of biliousness, ulcers, erysipelas, vomiting, vaginal complaints, fever, inflammations and leprosy. Its latex is said to be an aphrodisiac and tonic and also useful for healing wounds and lessening inflammations, for piles, nose diseases, and gonorrhea. The aerial root is used to treat syphilis, biliousness, dysentery and inflammation of the liver.

ESOTERIC

Comes with great love and transformative power. It has a high spiritual quality.

It brings contact with the light and the timeless eternal and the understanding of the unity of all life. Many different dimensions can be opened up by this remedy if you can let go.

It has an ethereal quality. The remedy has great beauty to it and at the same time is very delicate. A remedy of humbleness and purity, which is shy and sweet.

It keeps you linked to your spiritual path, your mission.

Allows contact with past and future and can be like a crystal ball.

Brings love, care, unity, harmony and the ability to use creativity. Links with creative energy, the love of the divine.

There is a lot of love and peace and gentleness and stillness with the remedy. Great stillness and peace. It can put people in touch with God and spirit when they have no idea of the existence of spirit. In that way it seems it can free people from the bondage of material life.

Allows you to breathe, have strong contact with God and brings you back to nature, simple things, simple understandings. Takes you away from intellectual understanding.

Helps you to follow your karmic path and be aware of, see in the mind's eye if not directly, the guides and guardian angels.

For very sensitive souls who cannot withstand the pressures of this earth realm. For those who wish to go or for those who have barely arrived. They are ethereal themselves.

It is a remedy which will help the earth herself where much healing is needed.

Allows the head to be in heaven and the feet on the earth, but helps those who have their feet on the earth to have their heads in heaven as well.

CHAKRAS

Powerful effect on all the chakras.

Releases the Upper Heart, Thymus, Upper Brow and Crown. Brings them into divine union.

Brings lovely energy around Throat and Sacral Centres.

Clears debris from the Thymus and heals the blueprint there.

Brings transformation, rebirth in the Heart Centre. Brings stillness, peace and expansive energy to the Heart Centre which encompasses the whole of the earth realm. This is the Garden of Eden, the Holy Grail.

It affords protection and much love. It is a good remedy for all those lacking in love, lacking the ability to express love.

Where the Heart Centre has closed off and there is no joy, they have become very weary and workworn. For those who are vulnerable in their state of mind and being.

CREATIVITY

There was a lot of singing and chanting, during the proving.

A magnificent beauty and natural spiritual expression of love through sexuality, through the creative expression of the voice in song, through music, painting, sculpting, poetry. Raises creative expression to its highest form.

Gives the opportunity to express love and creativity through the Sacral and Throat Centres.

Enhances whatever you do creatively within a group to be harmonised. Enables you to be able to walk round a group and make everyone feel safe.

It enhances the sharing of the expression of beauty within a group, such as a choir, orchestra, any performance.

For a loss of voice in any sense: spiritual, emotional, physical - the remedy can unblock many channels.

For those who've lost their voice, their expression. For those who've been dominated, especially women dominated by men.

It facilitates the release of emotion through the opening of the Throat and the voice.

DIVINE MOTHER & FEMININE ENERGY

Linked to the Great Mother, the Divine Mother, the Nurturer.

Connects to the energy that allows things to come into form, to become incarnate in flesh, to find expression in physical form.

Linked to the power of the moon, expressed through the Divine Mother. It releases moon energy and allows feminine energy to be expressed.

Time for us all to give birth to our gentler natures, helped by this remedy. Men have to learn to be more like women in this way.

Brings back sense of fun, joy, well-being, feminine healing energy, positive yin energy.

Much wisdom and strength, courage.

VISION & CLARITY

For clarity of vision. Gives the ability to see without emotion or prejudice that which is not healthy, which is false. Distinguishes between illusion and delusion. Gives clarity to see how to cope with a situation in a safe and secure way, all the things that feminine energy can do with so much love when it functions correctly.

Makes illusion and delusion much clearer, providing you are coming from a place of truth. Opens doors to other dimensions, other worlds, hidden energies that we have not been allowed to be see before.

LETTING GO

The remedy is good for helping people to let go and just to get on with what they have come here to do.

It brings a strong sense of forgetfulness, but where God lets you forget so you can let go of old hurts, upsets, traumas as they surface. The remedy enables you to let go of them so much that you have no memory of them.

It helps you to learn from experience and then let go.

Enables you to laugh, sing, to cry in a positive way. Brings you back to life, brings laughter and joy after the crying.

Very much for the future because it is about the return to God and energies becoming more ethereal and us becoming less material and less dense.

Helps us to leave the intellectualism of the past for the love of the heart of the future.

Liberates the spirit so you feel free and at peace. Things become clear. You let go of old ideas which no longer need to exist.

Very helpful in seeing what God is requiring of us now and letting go of old intellectualism and seeing the truth within the heart.

With the energies felt now things fall into the past very quickly and appear no longer significant. This enables us to create new frameworks for living, thinking and being.

LIBERATION

As the sun melts the snow on the peaks of the mountains, as the water moves the rocks down the mountains, this remedy brings liberation. Liberation is the key.

This remedy is for those who have eyes but do not see, those that have ears but do not hear, those that have voices but do not speak and for those that are stuck in their minds.

It liberates people from the bondage of everyday life for its own sake. Makes people's awareness of things so much greater.

Liberation and how it can really free you if you have faith and trust in God. Puts you back into contact with God and your source. You have to let go of all fear because fear is about not trusting God and not trusting in the process of love. Liberates you to be yourself and who God wants you to be. And under the umbrella of this energy, truth becomes revealed.

BABIES & CHILDREN

For creativity expressed as having a baby: the remedy brings harmony to the embryo, holds its energy in the centre of real love, protects the baby even if the mother is feeling ill or difficult.

Cleanses babies. For Calc Carbs with Brow problems, especially with sight.

For children who are locked within themselves and have difficulty in walking, talking, hearing and seeing.

GENERAL

For men who have completely lost their way and had a lot of dreadful things happen to them. They have lost their spirit and given up, perhaps if made redundant or been very ill. Can bring in energy and new spark, bring back their power and joy, so can see way forwards, enable them to find new direction.

Very good given to animals to help their suffering, to help strengthen their emotional bodies.

For a person or animal who is suffering loss or bereavement, pining away without love.

Gives protection and healing for all the left side of the body. The left side felt big and powerful, right side empty.

Helps pacify big egos; takes you out of the me and mine into the larger picture of unity.

Sharpens all the senses which allows us to be in the present moment.

PHYSICAL

Head: brings an essence of spiritual purity into the pituitary gland to remind the endocrine glands how to behave.

Ear: pain in L ear.

Heart: good for the heart. For valvular heart conditions, especially mitral stenosis. Powerful effect on all valves and where the heart is very tired. Old hearts, hearts of old people who are worn down and tired.

Heart attacks, hearts that have been traumatised.

Lowers cholesterol.

Lungs: for clearing debris from the lungs. Emphysema. Stasis at alveoli and at the top of the lungs.

Good asthma remedy.

Useful for smoke inhalation for those involved in fires.

Pain top of L lung.

Stomach: fear felt in the solar plexus.

Liver: drainage remedy.

Extremities: pins and needles in fingers and toes. Pain in L knee.

Valves: for all the valves anywhere in the body, in the veins, valves which have been non-functional, brings them back to life.

Good remedy for ileocaecal valve where there is stasis, between the junction of the two intestines.

Circulation: good for the veins and circulation, for piles, ulcers, varicose eczema.

CONNECTIONS

Affinity with England and Melchizedek.

With Neptune and illusion and delusion. This also represents the number 2.

Seven strong aspects to remedy, linked with seven energies of the White Brotherhood and seven circles of angels around group.

REMEDIES

Moonstone. Selenite. Mistletoe.

Strong connection with Chalcancite in fragility.

Very similar to the stability of Oak - feet firmly on the ground and the head in the heavens.

PRESCRIBING NOTES

Will do no harm to those not ready - will wait for them.

Bog Asphodel
Narthecium ossifragum

og asphodel is a member of the lily family, with yellow star-like flowers borne in a spike in July and warm orange fruit capsules lasting until September. It is often the only plant giving colour to boggy ground, and even into late autumn its dying leaves tint the ground orange. The yellow seeds have long tails at each end which help them to float and disperse in flood water. It is found throughout Northern Britain and North West Europe in wet or boggy ground and although it used to be a common plant it is now becoming scarcer as more wetlands are drained. The only folk use for it has been to produce a yellow dye and as a substitute for saffron. It used to have the reputation for causing bone damage in sheep, but this is now known to be due to the calcium deficient ground in which it prefers to grow rather than the plant itself.

Bog Asphodel is a flower essence for the willing slave, those who always help others to their own neglect and ignore their own needs. Such people can find it difficult to see that sometimes people who are suffering may need to work out their own salvation and imposed help can block the true healing process. Bog Asphodel people tend to be trapped by their emotional reactions to the suffering of others. The flower essence encourages people to take their missions in life more lightly and to avoid entanglements with the suffering of others. It helps us to take life more easily and find a more relaxed way of working.

ESOTERIC

Like a sword that cuts through illusion and delusion and reveals the truth: for those who live in a world of illusion and delusion.

Brings expansion and allows energy to rise upwards when it has been cut off at the lower levels.

Brings peace and stillness out of turmoil and strife.

Intense sense of light and enlightenment, exceptional lightness.

Extreme contrasts.

Releases syphilitic karma.

CHAKRAS

Heals the Thymus Chakra.

Blockage at the Brow Centre, producing dullness, slowness, like Calc Carb, slow thinking, slowness of learning. Slow to act. A state of imbecility.

A remedy for grief that rises from the Heart to Thymus, Throat and pituitary and gets locked in the Brow Centre.

ISOLATION & ABANDONMENT

A great sense of isolation, withdrawal, of being cut off, having no communication with others. Forsaken and abandoned.

Alone, rocking for comfort but there is no comfort. Getting no response. Cut off, ignored. Feeling of needing help and explanation. Knowing where help can be found but being ignored.

People who have deep old habits of being isolated, of cutting themselves off, where Natrum Mur and Sea Salt don't do enough.

Abandoned babies brought up in orphanages, adults with this terrible history that they can't ever get over. Early trauma of abandonment.

Children who have never been parented.

Release through this remedy of deep, deep karma which creates this situation. When the soul is ready this karma can be released and the lessons learned.

TRAPPED & STUCK

Sensation of being trapped. A state of having no expression, of being trapped in a body that can neither be left nor controlled.

Situations of stuckness, where patients don't get better, they go so far and go no further. Especially in children where you know they are stuck because of the parents.

Where a child is doing something because the parents won't, e.g. eczema because the child is manifesting the parents' problems.

Spasticity or any illness where the consciousness is present but the control is absent.

Vaccine damage, for autism where there is a lack of proper connection with the physical vehicle and where the soul cannot express its mission.

SEPSIS

Clears and cleanses down to the cellular level. Helps the regeneration of the cells.

States of blood poisoning affecting the extremities.

Hair loss, cellulitis, sepsis, toxic discharges. Teeth problems - rot and decay, abscesses.

Violent sweats. Convulsive, feverish states.

Burning pains.

EMOTIONAL

Very intense.

Violent states, a darkness, a sense of willful destruction.

For teenagers struggling with the dark side, looking for answers and feeling lost. Easily irritated, quick to anger, attracted to the bright lights, drug taking, alcohol. Take many risks. This remedy will help them to find their own purpose.

Enormous internal conflict.

A remedy for parents who cannot decide whether to vaccinate children or not. It will help them decide in the child's higher interest.

For those who wear a mask.

Helps those too caught up with business, work.

Anxieties caused by overwork and the sudden realisation that they have become isolated.

Desires company.

Wanting to sleep.

Anxiety. Completely churned up.

No sense of joy and lightness. Weary, plodding, like Calc Carb, just getting through it. A reluctance to carry on.

Complete detachment.

GENERAL

Burn out, depleted states. Lost, no energy. Blanked. Completely disordered with internal collapse. Deranged states. Extreme toxicity. The weakness centred on the solar plexus.

Dryness.

Thirstlessness.

Desire for cool, fresh air.

Lot of heat in the body and around throat especially. Burning sensation in solar plexus.

Deranged metabolism.

Problems from radiation.

Rocking.

Destructive in its action, similar to Phosphorus, for the erosion of healthy tissue.

Affects the calcium and phosphorus metabolism.

Left sided.

PHYSICAL

Head: for the pituitary, thyroid and parathyroid. L sided headaches.

Eyes: all eye conditions. L sided strabismus, converging. Eye strain. Blurred vision. Itching and swelling under the eye

Throat: sore throats < L side.

Neck: tension around shoulders and neck.

Female: R sided ovary.

Urinary: Bright's disease. Much to do with the water balance in the body. Fluid retention and excessive urination.

Nervous system: for the central nervous system. Repairs damaged nerves. Epilepsy. Parkinson's. MS.

Involuntary movements: with Parkinson's or after a stroke.

Back: pain, intense, heavy, pressing.

Extremities: swelling in the joints, especially the arms and hands, with heat < damp. Oedema, like Apis. Cold extremities.

Stinging in the centre of both palms

Pain on the left side.

MIASMS

Syphilitic.

REMEDIES

Lapis Lazuli. Berlin Wall. Phosphorus. Calc Phos. Kali Phos. Pulsatilla. Nux Vomica.

Brown Rice (Organic) Oriza sativa

Rice in its natural state contains an impressive array of vitamins and minerals, including calcium, iron, some zinc and the B vitamins Thiamine, niacin and riboflavin, magnesium, manganese, phosphorus, selenium, and even some vitamin E. It contains only a small amount of protein, but that is of good quality because of its relatively high content of the amino acid lysine. However, milling, which makes it white, has a profound effect reducing its thiamine by half. This is a hazard in the East where rice consumption is high and where only the poorest eat brown rice. Commercial interests have insisted on promoting polished rice largely because of its increased shelf life. Removing the layer of bran also removes the organic nutrients which are liable to decay but which give the rice its nutritional value. Brown rice is easily digested and high in insoluble fibre and therefore helpful in gastric and intestinal care. It is neither acid nor alkaline and has the reputation of being able to detoxify the body, providing the basic ingredient of gentle cleansing diets. It has even been recommended for cleansing crystals.

ESOTERIC

Dispels fear at birth and death. Allows souls to be released even through drugs.

Releases karma, enhances clairvoyance.

Releases deep grief, especially grief of groups, e.g. over the death of a public figure, the discharge of group karmic energy.

CHAKRAS

An affinity with all the chakras: it balances and harmonises.

Links into the energy of Saturn and grounds, but also Neptunian qualities - it unveils.

Sensation of constriction at the Solar Plexus.

Can clarify confused and blocked intuition from a Brow Chakra choked by comfort food.

CLEANSING

Great purification. Enormous cleansing on every level, so can have purging effect.

Cleanses blood and lymph. Blood poisoning and uraemia.

Purifies the gut. Encourages major organs to discharge toxicity.

Use for cleansing after viruses, from toxic overload, after poisons, from food poisoning, from anti-malaria drugs, from gas.

Helps to clear radiation toxicity.

NUTRITION & DIGESTION

Works on the whole of the alimentary canal. Calms inflammation; calms the liver, spleen and pancreas.

For nutrition and a compromised digestive system. Debility at every level from poor nutrition.

Food allergies.

Chemical imbalances in the body causing a split in functioning and toxicity. Has an effect on all trace elements - creates balance.

Influences calcium metabolism, hence growth and maturation.

For those who don't see how can they can help themselves by changing their diet. Helps people control what they eat. Comfort eating. Tendency to neglect diet. Restores appetite after a cold. Easily full even after ravenous appetite. Anorexia and bulimia. Increased appetite.

Desires things not normally eaten, e.g. meat, stimulants, sweets, alcohol, starch.

Craving for simple bland food.

Heavy stomach as of a brick in it. Grumbling appendix. Sygmoid flexure sore, distended.

Bloating, constipation, fluid retention < menopause, < menses, < eating a little, < starch. Yellow diarrhoea. Loose stools < 5am. Lienteric stools.

Worms, especially with ear problems. Candida, intestinal parasites.

GENERAL

A quiet hidden remedy of delicacy and refinement.

It gives backbone and strength.

It integrates Eastern understanding into Western minds.

For all states of transition: births on any level.

Helps to bring things to a conclusion and tie up loose ends. Where things come back from the past that had thought were finished.

Hormonal imbalances in men and women from nutritional problems, especially at puberty and the menopause. It balances oestrogen, progesterone and testosterone in both sexes. Hormone imbalances from polluted water.

Brown Rice

Autism and Aspergers.

Drowsy, sleepy, < after meals. Sleepy in the day, wakeful and restless at night.

Dreams of losing things, losing the way. Hot in bed.

Constricting and squeezing sensations: with asthma, from a difficult birth (especially breech), with kidney or gall stones, at the heart. For any situation in which there are feelings of being squashed and compressed, e.g. teenagers facing peer pressure. Constricting sensations accompanied by fear.

L sided.

Burning pains and discharges.

EMOTIONAL

Anxiety and fear: fear of change, of lack of routine, from routines being broken, of lack of discipline. Overwhelmed by anxiety but none can be identified.

Nervous and anxious but don't feel can ask for help. Self-contained.

Feeling lonely, lost and abandoned.

Makes people take responsibility for themselves and so removes fear.

For children frightened of their parents and teachers. Lonely children.

Fragile, spineless, don't want to be noticed, make an impression. Very sensitive, easily hurt, slighted, put off. Weak and helpless. 'Poor me'. Bowed down and negative. Humble but not servile.

Feels as if been thrown off balance and off course. Feels dislocated, displaced, out of the body sideways, lost.

Orderly, fastidious, need to do things in a proper, correct fashion (covers many scientists). Great attention to detail: works with small things. Precise and fastidious. Can become fetishists, superstitious, perform rituals.

No idea of how to help; stuck in a rut they can't see a way out of.

Unfocussed. Slow, difficult learning with defective nutrition and poor diet.

PHYSICAL

Head: integrates chemical and electrical energy in the brain, so good for brain injury and mental illness.

Poor memory. Memory loss especially after head injuries. Can't retain thoughts.

Vertigo, tendency to faint, feel light headed.

Head colds.

Ears: wax, especially in children. Loss of hearing, may be selective.

Eyes: cataracts.

Nose: thin, watery catarrh and snuffles. Loss of sense of smell.

Throat: catarrh in the throat, coughing, dryness, hard to swallow. No thirst.

Neck & spine: scoliosis and kyphosis. Stiff neck, spine cracks easily. Cracking and grinding of neck.

Kidneys: a drainage remedy for the for kidneys. Increased urine < night.

Female: birth trauma, breech birth. Fear in pregnancy.

Extremities: helps the flexion and articulation of tendons and ligaments. Weak and broken bones.

Skin: chronic skin: dryness, eczema, psoriasis, bed sores, ulcers, leprosy, mange, gangrene.

CONNECTIONS
Connects with no 7 made of 3 (spirit) and 4 (manifestation).

MIASMS
Calms the Sycotic miasm but also goes back to deep in the Psoric miasm and heals the ancestors.

REMEDIES
Okoubaka. Earthworm (its animal analogue). Medhorrinum. Natrum Mur. Baryta Carb. Psorinum. Chalcancite. Calc Sulph. Gaertner. Mimosa. Yellow. Phosphorous. Willow.

For childish states like Baryta Carb.

PRESCRIBING NOTES
A fast acting remedy and not necessarily gentle.

Antidoted by alcohol.

Buddleia Buddleia davidii

T his shrub, now a common naturalised shrubs in some places, is named after one Adam Buddle, a cleric and amateur botanist who died in 1715, although the plant was not introduced into this country until the early part of the 20th century. It originates in China and Japan where it grows in mountainous gravel and granite beds. Its long arching branches and slender, conical, purple flower heads are now a common sight in gardens and cities. It tolerates pollution well and has the ability to thrive in poor soil with almost no foothold. It is rarely seen in the open countryside, but grows like a weed in derelict urban areas, even growing through cracks in buildings where it would appear to have no sustenance at all. It grows rapidly and its nectar-rich flowers attract butterflies to such an extent that it is called the Butterfly Bush.

ESOTERIC

Brings Buddha's light and love to earth. Bliss. Christ consciousness.

Capacity to connect people with the spiritual source, to take them through their fear to a place of sanctuary and ultimately the lodge within the heart.

It is a remedy without limits, it reaches high up and low down.

Aid for constant meditation running through the heart of life not set aside for a special time only.

Integrates spirituality and spiritual awareness into life.

Helps where there is a deep sense of separation and brings boundaries where they are necessary, for those who feel lost because they have no boundaries.

Enhances all special senses. Refines and purifies not only the five senses, but the sixth and seventh also.

Affinity with eyes bringing clarity; for those who are wide eyed and too open as well as being able to open those who are too closed.

Lets everything else drop away leaving only clarity

Keeps you calm and centred from the Heart and also can provide a shock to put you back on the path if lost.

Following the law of nature rather than the law of man.

Helps us contact the plant divas, especially the spirits of the trees.

Connected with growth - the spiritual metamorphosis which it facilitates.

Helps release us from ancestral bondage.

Feminine energy in the very broadest sense. It is receptive.

Balance between power and beauty, or liberty and necessity.

Lack of control. Sense that all vehicles were loose and being lifted up.

Give spiritual courage. Helps people cross the abyss and its action is quite gentle, like waves rippling out.

For those energies, human and divine, who have been lost in abyss, will bring them back to light.

CHAKRAS

Links heaven and earth, Base, Crown and Heart.

Harmonises and joins the mind-body link through the Heart.

Integrates Base and Crown.

Keeps us grounded while maintaining a link through the Crown.

Strengthens Base Chakra.

Makes it safe for Kundalini to rise and helps it to.

Opens the Crown with safety and protection.

Sensation of pressure at the Upper Brow.

Brow Centre, Throat and Base.

Allows you to open the Heart Centre for true understanding and love, for you must bear no malice or resentment to any of your brothers as you move on.

TRAUMA

A powerful remedy for shock and trauma which has infiltrated the being on all levels, including the spiritual.

Works in a very powerful but gentle way, releasing layers of trauma and fear.

Its effect is to clear deep fear, shock and trauma from the psyche and remove the mutated symptoms of such.

This shock and fear and trauma can be from many lifetimes ago, for the psyche holds at all times the experience of past lives.

The effect of these traumas will gently leave your being and weights will feel lifted from you, allowing you to feel deep, deep peace and allowing you to surrender, which is at all times the only way forward.

Shock can often be seen in the aura as black 'ectoplasm' furring the higher centres and blocking communication with life.

Unless the seed of trauma is removed from the aura, the individual cannot completely live.

Buddleia

It can heal not only the individual's karma but also that of and their ancestors. It can heal even to the soul source. Has the ability to shift deep karmic patterns, to bring them to the surface where they can be seen and released.

Useful where there has been a shock from a previous incarnation and the effects are still apparent in this incarnation. Can work deeply.

For those in deep shock who do not want to take on life's task.

Coma. It will help maintain alignment and integrity of the higher bodies in a coma. It carries on working where Arnica stops.

Especially good given to any patient who has been in a hospital environment where there is little healing light and where their spirit will have taken on much trauma from other beings.

Helps heal the wounds and traumas we have created to the earth. Can be added to the water, sprinkled on the land.

A great injury remedy.

Specific to never-been-well-since blow to the head, especially the sides.

For birth trauma generally. Effects of birth trauma where the skull is compressed at the sides, like a forceps delivery.

Mute after a shock or a blow.

The effects of electric shock treatment.

After road traffic accidents.

FEAR

Homeopathic tranquiliser.

Brings peace and a great degree of trust and faith that everything is perfect the way it is.

States of extreme anxiety focussed in the back of the throat and in the solar plexus.

Primordial fear going back to being banished from The Garden.

For those who cannot move forward without fear, who feel powerless, who choose to run away.

Paralysed by terror.

Panic attacks.

For people addicted to light and afraid of the dark.

A great remedy for anticipatory fears and tensions, forebodings. For children with anticipatory fear. Anticipation felt in the stomach

Brings peace and clarity for people to relax into what is ahead of them.

Fear of being oneself.

Helps remove the fear of going into one's own light or power if the soul is indeed willing and ready to make that change. In these cases will initially calm the individual and help them to see.

Fear of incarnating.

Fear of the dentist or hospitals.

BIRTH & DEATH

A remedy for the transition in and out of incarnation.

Difficult birth created by the fear of the incarnating soul. Helps incarnating souls arrive on earth in peace and tranquillity.

With Orange, Sandalwood and Ether, a remedy to help the soul leave the physical body.

Brings infinite peace to the person who is passing over and to their relatives, shedding light and showing that there is no separation.

DETACHMENT

Detachment, isolation, withdrawing into the self, not connecting with the Heart Centre.

Sensation of stillness when this is perceived negatively.

Stuckness and an inability to move forward.

Stilled emotions so that nothing is felt directly.

Detachment without sympathy although knows the feeling is there somewhere.

For those anaesthetised by gruesome things.

Deeply held grief and pain in the Heart, Thymus and Throat where the stillness acts to protect it and hide it where it is not felt.

Helps release a lot from this bound up state.

An inability to communicate from a failure to make connection, there is simply nothing to say.

CHILDREN

Helps children to become aware of spiritual contact where this broken.

Helps children make sense of their education, to understand their path.

Heals the effects of sexual abuse.

Heals the effects of bitter criticism received as a child.

Buddleia

For all those who have had to hide in order to grow, to hide inside or physically hide. Heals the effects of a despairing childhood.

It is very good for separation of the mother and child when the bond needs to be broken and neither side can break it. Closely linked to Folliculinum.

Down's Syndrome children.

FATHERS

For children who don't know who their fathers are.

Children growing up believing their father to be someone else.

For children who have had no male energy in their lives.

Those who have no psychic connection or link, who have lost that contact with the father. Releases some of this sadness.

The remedy can't help the fathers because in this lifetime they are not able to do this.

It releases the grief and heals those who have been emotionally or physically abused by their fathers.

MENTAL

Non-development of mental and emotional faculties, follows routines and does what is expected.

Mental blockage.

Children who stare vacantly in a classroom. Don't understand why they are there. Electrical connection broken. Head and brain clogged. Brings clarity.

Chattering mind: prevents people from getting on and achieving; want to sleep to shut it out.

EMOTIONAL

Heals deep distress. Makes you feel safe and wanted and secure.

Those who do not nurture themselves, who are self-critical and give themselves a hard time, who think they are never good enough.

Brings peace, calmness and tranquility, a homeopathic relaxation.

Calm and the peace and wisdom after the storm of passion is spent, passion about anything.

Stabilising, balancing and creative.

People who find it difficult to cry; want to cry but can't.

For those who are burdened: bowed down, shoulders and spine bent with worry and adversity. Strengthens and straightens.

For those who have lost their backbone metaphorically, lost the ability to walk upright on all levels. Remedy will lift and strengthen a broken spirit and bring joy back into the soul.

Brings light from out of the gloom; helps in real total despair.

Gives protection.

Brings playfulness, lightness, joyfulness, singing. Brings light where there is no hope; brings joy where there is sorrow and strength where there is weakness.

For those with big egos.

Encourages generosity in those who have achieved and helps them to give.

Gives us the ability to turn over a new leaf, make a fresh start.

Those stuck in routines, needing the will and the motivation to seek something new and different.

Dreams of being out of control with frustration at not being able to do anything about it.

Mid-life crisis, where what is needed is spiritual meaning.

Helps people to see better what is going on in their lives and around them and so make better judgements.

Useful for times when there are big decisions to be made, life choice points like a job.

Gives vision and detachment.

GENERAL

Works well before a general anaesthetic so this only touches the physical body. Modern anaesthetics are more dangerous than in the past and have a very damaging constitutional effect.

Excellent for syphilitic cancers in any part of body. Once given to the patient it will also help practitioner to see clearly.

Unties knots on all levels: in joints, in extremities, in rheumatics and arthritics, in the stomach, in the nerves.

Protects the nervous system. Connects the brain with the spine and nervous system.

Complete physical degeneration, broken down states. Wastage, emaciation and withering, with age or otherwise.

M.E. - simply fading away, almost emotionally fading away.

No sense of where the body is in space. Arms and legs feel big.

PHYSICAL

Head: headaches. Heavy head.

Good for brain tumours and hard nodules in and around the head.

L face, teeth and ear painful and numb.

Eyes: excellent for all pathology around ears and eyes and hypothalamus blockages.

For tumours in and behind the eyes.

Sticky eyes. Cataract. All levels of vision.

Ears: R ear - pressure and blockage, as if numbed; L ear - as if down a tube.

Mouth: after dental work.

Neck: gland swollen on L.

Stiff neck and shoulders. Clicking and crunching necks.

Higher aspects at the thyroid and pituitary.

Thyroid malfunction, lack of balance, especially where it involves the pituitary.

Breast: tumours.

Lungs: asthma. Tumours.

Heart: hypertensive states which yield to no other remedy. Enables the heart to breathe and see and understand again.

Skin: burns of all sorts - radiation, skin cancer, ordinary burns. Heals burn wounds quicker and decreases level of keloid scarring.

Skeleton, muscles & joints: major area of use is on spine and skeletal structure. Physical injuries to and all physical disorders of the spine.

Bones. Joints.

Cranial osteopathy.

Swelling, lack of connection, lack of muscle tone, tears in muscles, ankle sprains, swollen knees.

Paralysis; inability to move forward.

Severe pain R shoulder under the scapula.

Legs are weak and bent, physically or spiritually, gives strength and uprightness.

Sensation of heat down the back.

Fluids & kidneys: cleanses and purifies all the fluids in the body - mucus, lymph, water.

Strong affinity with the water balance in the body and the kidneys.

Homeopathic diuretic. Kidney stones.

Watery cysts from the bottom of the body and hard, dark nodules at the top of body.

Waterlogged swelling, fluid retention, bloating.

Sexual: disorders of the female organs, especially where there is sensitivity to moon phases. Fibroids, menstrual disorders, excessive loss of blood, black blood, endometriosis.

Period pains where a woman has a difficult relationship with her mother.

Good in childbirth.

Deep healing of sexuality.

CONNECTIONS

Blue and mauve. Grey.

The number 10.

The path from Tiphareth to Gebura. Path of light. Courage.

MIASMS

Syphilitic miasm.

Has the possibility of working more deeply than Syphilinum, for it goes beyond that level of trauma. Can work well to assist it. You will be surprised what you will see once this is given, for that which lies beyond what is hidden by the syphilitic miasm can truly, truly heal the spirit on many levels.

REMEDIES

Lycopodium - desire for material and status but unlike Lycopodium, there is an unwillingness to venture out and get it.

Clear Quartz. Rose Quartz. Phantom Quartz. Black Obsidian. Clay. Sycamore. Earthworm. Aconite. Diamond. Pearl. Lotus. Silver Birch. Phosphorus.

Follows Oak and all the Base Chakra remedies.

Copper Beech - life is withering away without achievement; premature ageing; also related to Conium.

Buddleia

Sequence of Natrum Mur, then Sea Salt, then Buddleia.

Use with Natrum Mur and Lachesis, with Belladonna and Agaricus.

Lies between Aurum Met and Argentum Met emotionally.

Arnica+Syphilinum+Buddleia is a very powerful combination for deep shock.

With Phantom Quartz for the shock brought in from a previous incarnation.

PRESCRIBING NOTES

Give the remedy when the patient cannot tell you their symptoms, don't know what the problem is, they say superficial things and cannot access the depths of their being.

Helps prescriber to see different angle to a case. Removes prejudice and allows perception of what remedy is needed.

Good remedy to be given with all present remedies for physical and emotional trauma. It will enable them to work much more deeply, to work on the spiritual trauma which blocks so deeply.

In lower potency useful as a cleanser and protector as used in an atomiser.

Butterfly (Red Admiral - Vanessa Atalanta)

T *he butterfly has been used as symbol for the spirit or soul for thousands of years; the ancient Greeks used the same word for both -* psyche. *It signified the fulfillment of man's destiny and the transition from earthly to heavenly life. Many cultures see the butterfly as embodying the incarnating or dying soul. For Native Americans, it was the symbol of transformation and resurrection.*

We associate the butterfly with the mind: we say someone has a 'butterfly mind' if they have a short concentration span and flit from one interest to another. We never say someone has a 'butterfly heart' if he or she is emotionally inconstant and moves quickly from one relationship to another. The imago, the name given to the final butterfly stage, comes from the Latin meaning image, which also relates to the mind, the places where we create images, the seat of our imagination.

Most butterflies are masters of camouflage which is usually their only defence. When their wings are closed they often look like the leaves or twigs on which they feed. This could be seen as connecting them to the Syphilitic miasm, characterised by conditions which are hidden and not what they seem.

Butterflies cannot transmit diseases to humans as they are so different from us physiologically and they do not carry diseases. They appear to flit about but in fact fly thousands of miles and in straight lines. They are very territorial and what we interpret as pairs of butterflies dancing are in fact territorial fights. Each species of butterfly is usually dependent on one or two plants on which the eggs are laid and on which the larvae (caterpillar) feed when they hatch. Consequently they are very vulnerable to changes of climate and habitat.

The Red Admiral butterfly has nothing to do with the navy but is a corruption of Red Admirable, its original name. It is widespread from North America through Europe, Asia and N. Africa. Although common in Britain and Ireland in almost any habitat from mountain to seashore, it is in fact a seasonal migrant. The adult butterflies have a tendency to hibernate in exposed places and so very few manage to overwinter in Britain. Those that do, survive mainly in ivy. They breed early in the year in Spain and North Africa. Those adults and their offspring continue to move northwards with the improving weather, breeding as they go, sometimes reaching Britain in small numbers as early as March. There are often large numbers of butterflies here in the autumn through to October and November. Their numbers are increasing.

Each newly arrived male defends its chosen territory vigorously. The eggs are laid singly on the upper leaves of nettles - usually in the middle of large patches and the female takes no further care of them. Each female can lay two broods in a season.

After about seven days the larva emerges and immediately folds a leaf together to make 'tent', securing the edges with silk. Within this structure the young caterpillar can feed in relative safety. Several leaf tents are made as the caterpillar grows, shedding its skin, each progressively larger. The spiny caterpillars come in two colour forms - black and a yellow green, both with yellow markings down each flank. When fully grown the caterpillar chews part way through a nettle stem causing it to fall over. It then spins together several of these, now downward pointing, leaves to create a shelter in which to pupate. This is the chrysalis stage. The adults emerge from the chrysalis, which is patterned with metallic gold spots, in approximately 12 days as the imago or adult butterfly. Late in the season, any flower-rich habitat is likely to attract the butterfly, including gardens where buddleias, stonecrops, and Michaelmas-daisies are all popular with Red Admirals. They also favour orchards where fruit is rotting on the ground.

ESOTERIC

Will help people into consciousness of the Aquarian Age.

Helps those who are earthbound to open up their spirituality.

Manifestation of Divine Grace.

Takes consciousness to new level, the power of experiencing God's kingdom on earth. Direct link with Divine energy, with Angels, Archangels and St Germain.

Helps you to be still and know God. Enhances meditation and focus.

Promotes creativity: through the mind and imagination, through the use of the voice and the physical creation of children.

CHAKRAS

Brings Brow, Throat and Sacral chakras into balance.

Balances the Brow and Heart energies.

Expansion of Brow and Crown Chakras, with grounding and connection to the Soul Star.

Stimulates energy and chakras above the Crown.

A lot of energy and expansion experienced at the Throat Chakra.

Balances the Throat and Sacral chakras during the menopause.

Links the Throat Chakra and pancreas.

RELEASE OF DARKNESS

Reaches from the heights to the depths: touches the most depraved levels of consciousness and human nature and also rises to the heights of divine love.

Needed for the darkest recesses of the soul, the darkest of karmas, for those who have done great evil either in this life or past lives, who carry with them awful responsibilities for what they have done.

Accesses and clears pockets of negative energy, especially in those souls who are otherwise evolved and functioning at a high vibration.

Goes back into karmic and ancestral past.

TRANSITION & TRANSFORMATION

Enormous transformation. Transitions, growth and development on all levels.

Allows the letting go of the past so there is space for the new to come in.

Dying and birthing.

Can enable those in positions of power to see the light for the first time. For powerful men. Will allow politicians and people in power to change and adjust and do things new.

OPENING OF THE HEART

A big Heart opening remedy. Much love in all the provings.

Linked to the birth of the Christ in the Heart in gentleness, peace - qualities given by this remedy.

Removes fear from the Heart, removes the need for judgement and makes you more understanding and accepting of others - the expression of unconditional love of the opened heart.

Stops the Heart Chakra from closing down after loss or bereavement.

Heavy heart, heartache, broken heart. Recovery from loss and bereavement - heart feels bruised & fragile.

Sensation of a cold rod or an ice crystal at the Heart Chakra.

For people who need to learn how to accept love. Allows those suspicious about love to see the truth.

Those who have been scapegoated, betrayed, where they have shut down as a result.

Very few symptoms for the physical heart. Agitation of the heart alternates with calmness and serenity.

SADNESS & DEPRESSION

Depressed. Future holds nothing. Stuck. Can't see way forward.

For those living in the material world, cut off from higher self, spirit, who think all that stuff is nonsense, but have no joy in anything.

Sense of disconnection, isolation, abandonment, inability to reach out to another, unhappy.

Those who discover something is not as they thought it to be.

Releases trauma locked in throat. Constriction of throat, desire to cry but can't.

Morbid thoughts cannot get rid of - e.g. that husband dead. So tired and depressed that when I came out of the proving there were ten loads of washing to do and no food in house.

THE BROW CHAKRA & THE MIND

Opens the mind. A thirst, a craving for spiritual knowledge. Awakens inner sight.

Stimulates intuition, clairvoyance and the imagination.

Enables those who work with the imagination to bring through higher levels of their creativity.

Affects thinking. Helps to bring people out of mental dominance. Gives an understanding of power of thought and creative use of thought.

Loss of ability to think, act, no motivation, depression, loss of spiritual contact.

Inability to meditate through mental activity

Balances Heart and Brow. Power of Brow offered in service to Divine Child of Heart.

MENTAL ILLNESS

Schizophrenia and other forms of mental illness - split in consciousness.

Separation from the Source, of the personality from the soul, of the soul from the body.

Mental confusion, congestion, chaos, madness connected with the spilling of blood.

Teenagers where there is confusion and a loss of sense of reality.
Sensation of things being surreal.

For creative people - poets, artists, musicians - who get stuck, end up in their heads, become mad, possibly schizophrenic.

Will help release potential for madness.

PERSONAL POWER

Releases people from low expectations of themselves.

Opens you to contacting your own power. Brings in personal power by allowing the individual to contact the higher aspects of soul.

Gives the ability to become greater than we ever thought we could, pushes back personal horizons. Expands our potential, who we think we can be. Gives permission to be yourself, to do your soul purpose.

Gives resolution, determination not to succumb to failure of confidence.

RELATIONSHIPS & MALE/FEMALE ENERGY

A great healer of relationships between sexes.

Detachment in relationships causing problems with partners. Issues about communication and not communicating - giving up, not bothering to try.

Integrates and balances masculine and feminine energy.

Helps in transformation of relationships and balance of male/female energy both in the individual and between couples.

Balances out the aggressive tendencies which have been playing out through the female consciousness, allowing finer feminine energy to be contacted. Allows masculine energy to awaken and relax.

Balances out both extremes.

CHILDREN

A great remedy for new children coming in.

Can seem like Calc Carb, Silica: shy, slow, followers not leaders. Will help them to walk their own path.

Children who are sickly and delicate, not eating well or not utilising food they are eating. Will improve appetite and nutrition.

Arrested growth in children in any area. Delayed maturation, height, etc.

Will help children incarnating with cancer already grafted on to them from a previous incarnation.

NERVOUS SYSTEM

A lot of symptoms in this area especially numbness and paralysis. Profound effect on the nervous system.

Numbness, tingling, delusion of size, phantom pains, the refusal of the body to obey the will through nerve degeneration.

Spasticity - soul not in control of the body.

Cases of MS that defy diagnosis or where the diagnosis and the symptoms do not agree, or where the symptoms are unusual for the diagnosis.

Ability to regenerate nerves especially useful in children badly damaged in accidents, brain damaged at birth through physical trauma not through lack of oxygen; after brain surgery.

Sensation as if hands huge, heavy, numb, tingly, weighing me down.

Tingling of fingers and L arm.

Legs feel very heavy.

Limbs contracted, nervous system is on 'go' all the time.

Damage or disease affecting the nerves of the spine.

Shooting pains in L side.

Twitching under the eye.

EMOTIONAL

An amplifier of conscience.

Helps with balance between being an individual and being part of a group - very important for the Aquarian Age. Good for teenagers who are drawn along with the crowd.

Those who feel bound by convention or by other people's expectations.

Inertia which may only be overcome by act of will. Too tired to fight.

Loss of purpose and direction, doubt and anxiety, lack of confidence.

Blows away fear and terror even if they were hidden.

Loosens, frees, joins.

For those who find it difficult to let go, change, be flexible.

Encourages optimism and positive thinking.

GENERAL

Integration of the whole being on all levels. A sense of relaxing and opening.

Helps stabilise the body on all levels for receiving new energies and allows them to be anchored.

General heaviness, sluggishness, tiredness, lethargy.

Likes damp.

Feelings of heat. Also cold - chill moves inwards < wrapping up.

Rolling, falling to the left, feeling bigger and bigger, like a paralysis as well.

Effects of vaccination, in particular meningitis and measles vaccines.

The power to release enormous darkness manifesting in deep pathology.

Can help to release people from traumas of chemotherapy and given before, may stop them having it.

PHYSICAL

Head: a lot of headaches, pains in the head and symptoms around the head.

For all kinds of head pathology: headaches, brain tumours, brain inflammations. Heaviness of head.

Great compression in head, like tight hat/helmet, sometimes with nausea, like migraine.

Headaches especially around L eye, nose, face, ear, neck and shoulder.

Very light at the top of the head. Sudden surge of dizziness.

Face: feels congested and heavy. Great stuckness in the head, nose bunged up, post nasal drip.

Eyes ache. Eyes and nose ache.

Tingling in teeth, to do with amalgam fillings, electricity in the mouth.

Neck: lots of neck stiffness, crunching, cracking. Tense neck and shoulders. Frozen shoulder.

Throat: profound effect on the thyroid especially thyroid problems in puberty and menopause.

Throat and upper chest constricted.

Throat full of mucous. Tacky throats. Throat painful, raspy and burning.

Abdomen: lots of diarrhoea. Bowels loose, stools very small, barely formed. Nausea.

Female: excellent menopause remedy. Hot flushes.

Sharp pain R ovary extending to back of pelvis, stabbing pain, comes and goes.

Butterfly

Female fertility problems; will help with ovulation, establish cycle.

Earthbound, materially minded women, mentally tied to work, unable to conceive.

Useful during labour, especially for children finding it difficult to incarnate i.e. difficult birth.

Skeletal: powerful effect on bones, joints, structure of the body.

Stiffness in the neck and extremities, especially fingers.

Rheumatic pains in fingers and joints.

Pain - ache, over right hip and adjacent part of the back.

Spine: back feels squashed, compressed. Spine feels numb.

Sleep: dreadful.

Dreams: of being chased by an alligator; of someone being pregnant and taking it in turns to do the labour: I did my turn really well and the baby was being born; of being late, running, manic, being lost, escaping from danger.

CONNECTIONS
To the individual and universal blueprints.

MIASMS
Syphilitic

REMEDIES
Chalice Well. Clay. With Pearl at Throat Chakra. With Blue for the nervous system.

Works in a totally different way from Earthworm and the two remedies won't work together.

For the nervous system. Here the vegetable analogue is Cotton, the mineral is Ametrine.

PRESCRIBING NOTES
Quick in action. Can be repeated frequently. Use alone, alongside other remedies or in combination. Will speed up all processes of change.

Can be used alongside remedies for the worst pathology. Without the underlying state being addressed, pathology will not be released. Not all will be able to make this release, but at least it gives the soul the choice.

Cotton Boll

C otton has been produced and woven for thousands of years; pieces of cotton cloth at least 7,000 years old have been found by archeologists in Mexico and cotton was being woven in Pakistan 5,000 years ago. Arab merchants brought cotton to Europe about 800 CE and Columbus found cotton already growing in America in 1492. By the 1450s, cotton was known throughout the world. The first settlers in America grew cotton and until the industrial revolution it was a poor white man's crop. It was the mechanisation of the spinning and weaving processes from the end of the 18th century, in particular the development of the cotton gin to separate the seeds out of the cotton fibre, that fuelled the slave trade for the growing of cotton in America. This in turn powered the industrialisation of the north of England for cotton spinning and weaving in the 19th century.

Varieties of cotton have now been developed to grow on any soil and it has also been genetically modified. As a crop it is highly dependent on chemical pesticides and fertilisers and has a depleting effect on the soil. The cotton trade has been linked not only with the infamy of slavery in the past but also with the continued exploitation of the Third World.

Cotton fibre comes from the cotton plant's seed pod. It is hollow in the centre and under a microscope looks like a twisted ribbon. Absorbent cotton will retain about 25 times its own weight of water and is stronger when wet than dry. It absorbs and releases perspiration quickly, thus allowing the fabric to breathe. Cotton can stand high temperatures, takes dyes easily, stands up to abrasion and wears well. It also takes to many different weaves and finishes - there are least 24 commonly produced, ranging from muslin for babies' nappies to duck for tents and sails. It is often blended with other fibres and is still one of the most popular of materials. Once one of the most expensive of fabrics, it is now one of the cheapest.

The cotton for this remedy came from southern Spain and was taken just before harvesting in November. Only the white cotton boll was used.

ESOTERIC

Remedy attracts incredible power from other spheres and must be received in a different way. Reaches into other levels of consciousness.

Remedy goes to the very centre of the being. It is pure love and light. Peace and harmony.

A universal healer. Brings protection and peace.

Increases the vibration of the physical, etheric and spiritual bodies.

Brings lightness and joy. Linked to fairies and etheric kingdoms.

Brings the clarity we need to use new remedies in the New Age.

Promotes bonding in groups, harmony in groups, helps people leave behind their egos so they can work for common good.

Brings desire for spiritual awareness in those who are closed and opens even further those on spiritual path. Helps us to grow spiritually. Put us back on the path we were destined for. Brings Soul connection and Soul growth.

Makes people aware of their mission in life and so can cause upheavals. Brings out karmic issues. Helps lighten the load we all carry.

Keeps you going when at the point of losing faith. Would bring back the people who have lost their way and their connection with God. For lost souls.

Helps break down rigid structures in people's lives which have held them there for so long, set in their ways. Gently shows that what was important is no longer important.

Releases desire and attachment. Will reveal hidden or suppressed thoughts and emotions so people will creatively be able to explore life at its fullest.

CHAKRAS

Changes your vibration profoundly. Brings in completely new energy and an opening of all the Centres. Removes deep blocks from the past.

Heart Centre and spine.

The colours blue and green and the Thymus Centre. The remedy can bring about powerful sense of self.

Base Centre.

Seat of this remedy is not just the Base Centre but the Brow, Pituitary, Pineal and Third Eye generally.

Brow Centre and sleep.

For those blocked at the Throat where the energy cannot rise. People stuck emotionally at the Throat e.g. from grief. Helps women going through the menopause by opening the Throat Centre.

GROUNDING

It is for grounding people. Gentle strength and grounding. Those who are spaced out so cannot be themselves.

Puts feet on the ground, head in the heavens.

Basic remedy. Encourages patient to go back to basics, to simplify life.

For people who are trapped in their heads - too much energy in the head. People who have trouble staying in the present, connecting with the earth.

Out of body through drug use - medical or recreational. Those out of their bodies because the kundalini rose too quickly. Will reintegrate the subtle bodies.

For those who are self-absorbed and self-conscious: helps them to become self-aware and let go of old ideas of themselves. Helps ground people to reveal their true potential.

THE HEART

Peace in the heart.

Opens the heart with feelings of protection and safety.

Restores identity in the truest sense, from the heart.

Brings absolute truth, integrity and an open heart.

Brings to people a moral consciousness and awareness of the heart in developing and using new technologies.

PURIFICATION

Refining quality on every level. Purifies to very high levels.

Purification of consciousness.

Releases much of other dimensions that require healing.

Energy of remedy can undo a lot of the damage we've done to our planet, as if it deals with petrified beings, structures.

Helps remove radiation toxicity.

For the effects of nuclear disasters and souls stuck and lost as a result of radiation.

Genetic mutation from radiation resulting in deformation of sense organs especially.

ENERGY, INERTIA & PARALYSIS

Dullness on every level (marked).

Paralysis is a strong symptom of the remedy on every level: mental, emotional, physical.

Awareness but no connection. No emotion, completely flat.

Mind wandering.

Mind blank, worse than Baryta Carb.

Cannot be bothered to answer or communicate

Paralysed with inactivity. Would be better if cried but not enough energy, can't be bothered.

Stuck, lack of inspiration, no intuition. Not able to make connections with other people, but not being cut off, just simply not being able to reach out very well.

The weak and timid. Gives courage. For lack of courage, reticence, timidity.

People who have had a bad stroke: awareness there but no control of body.

The inertia and stillness before breakthrough to the next part of the journey

Inertia, sort of sinking feeling as if cannot be bothered to hold it together. Sense of why bother.

Helps in raising energy and enthusiasm and the ability to direct it in life, to be able to put it to some positive purpose.

A very peaceful and gentle energy. Peace connected to energy of Mars and remedy for over-abundant Martian energy. Calms aggression, violence, rage. Brings great peace and serenity. Helps people stop hustling, bustling and feeling pressured and to focus energy, get back on path and stop dissipating their energy. Gives rest.

Works with great gentleness and great power.

PITUITARY GLAND & ENDOCRINE SYSTEM

Helps balance the whole of the endocrine system. By healing the endocrine system, the nervous system is given a new spark, the immune system and the liver and spleen are activated.

Dull with a faulty endocrine system and body clock, from a great deal of life experience.

Solar plexus is dragging, is heavy, is in need of a detox, not as the primary source of the pathology, but as a result of the endocrine system being sluggish. The same is true of the uterus and ovaries. Everything is dull.

Strong connection with the pituitary gland.

Benign tumours of the pituitary.

Not growing at the normal rate.

BRAIN

A powerful remedy for the brain and nerves.

Remedy will create new neural pathways in brain.

Could feel and hear head, brain and skull moving.

A remedy for children, where the brain is not fixed.

Needs a child to interpret the energy of the remedy correctly.

Remedy acts like a diamond in the brain: brings clarity, clearness and sharpness.

Whole of primitive brain is affected.

NERVOUS SYSTEM

Fortifies and empowers the nervous system in a way that goes beyond something like Kali Phos, whilst maintaining a grip upon the earth.

It works well on the nervous system where there is injury of the higher centres. It clears the nerve pathways. Use it where there is paralysis especially the arms, the right side especially the face and arm.

Nerve regeneration.

Paralysis.

Would be good for people with M.S. and M.E. because they are not able to harness that direct enthusiasm or zeal or motivation. Parkinson's disease.

Relaxes tense muscles, relieves spasms and helps people deal with stress.

Muscular rigidity and a kind of paralysis, almost inertia in those who have not developed their full potential.

EMOTIONAL

Helps jealousy, especially jealousy between children.

For the first child displaced by the second.

Children who feel pushed out and don't get the attention they want and need.

Bereavement.

Sense of futility. Helps to support us in times of difficulty where we do not understand what is happening and why - that the soul is growing and learning. It can give strength and understanding. A sense of things too difficult. Very tired of it all.

Gradual feeling of depression and futility. Sobbing heart out, but also angry and frustrated.

Morbid and a bit miserable. Depressed by ageing.

Wanting to cry, but too much effort. (marked in the proving)

Sadness and blankness.

Fed up, can't be bothered, why try? I'm a failure, so why bother? Self-pity.

Impatient.

Seriousness.

For the person who always jokes, doesn't take things seriously, makes flippant and inappropriate comments. Underneath is a despair, deep hurt that is hidden; very male energy.

GENERAL

Experimentation on human tissue, where autopsies are done and parts of the body are taken unknown to the relatives. [Place on the body or send through prayer. Ed.]

Strong and powerful cleansing of the DNA.

Healing after lasers and surgery.

Cholesterol and clearing out of arteries.

Agitation, debility. Adrenal exhaustion. Sexual dysfunction. States of weakness - legs weak and wobbly. Light headedness. Imbalance in sugar metabolism.

Lack of oxygen making everything dull.

Leaning to the left.

It brings coolness to burning pains.

Premature hair loss in men and women.

Balances male and female energy.

PHYSICAL

Head: pain occiput, clenching, tension. Headaches from injury.

Eyes: nystagmus. Cataracts. No colour. Colour blindness. Vision not sharp or bright. Physical degeneration of the eyes. Where the fluid balance in the eye is upset.

Throat: throat closed, catarrh.

Throat sore, tight, clenched, leading to pain R ear.

For thyroid and associated weight problems.

Ear: deep pain R ear connected with tongue.

Lungs: asthma, difficult breathing.

Irritation of larynx and coughing.

Lung cancer esp. where throat is also affected.

Constriction of lungs.

Closely aligned to the breath, helps attunement of breath in meditation and deepens awareness of breath.

Abdomen: swelling abdomen, not > flatulence.

Works on organs of digestion: spleen, stomach, liver, pancreas.

Diabetes, too much sugar in the blood.

Sensation in the solar plexus like that of fear.

Haemorrhoids.

Frequent stools.

Sleep: waking early, lying awake, 5am.

Inappropriate wakefulness. Sleep disturbances.

Body clock not working, out of synch. For night workers, shift workers.

Tumours & cancer: pre-cancerous cell changes.

Benign tumours. Growths. Cancer. Can help reduce cancerous tumours very effectively. Can soak up negativity and transmute it.

Catarrh: lot of catarrh, thick and heavy.

Children mouth breathing and snuffling and not filling the lungs fully, shallow breathing, Glue ear and galloping catarrh.

CONNECTIONS

The remedy resonates with the number 2.

Link with India.

Thrones with religious connections, a bishop's throne, a king's throne.

About the incarnating DNA and related to three ascending powers of the spine.

Related to the colour blue.

A red orb and an eagle.

MIASMS

Can help people to heal their cancer miasm by leading them back to psora.

Strongly linked to the hereditary impact of past generations. Cancerous miasm. DNA.

Very tubercular, sycotic and psoric.

Cotton

REMEDIES

Use in combination with Carcinosin. Carcinosin and this remedy and one other (possibly Arsenicum) can heal the cancer miasm in those whose family bear cancer strongly.

Corn would open this remedy.

Sunflower. Snowdrop. Sulphur. Carcinosin. Lycopdium. Goldfish. Sequoia - gentle giant.

Baryta Carb is complementary.

Connection with Clay in feelings of inadequacy.

Works well with Earthworm in breaking down old structures.

Can be used with the plant kingdom remedies.

PRESCRIBING NOTES

Use with those sensitive to electric frequencies, power cables, sub-stations and mobile phones.

A remedy for people who have become exhausted. Healers who have given out - not recharged their batteries.

Gentle, long and deep acting.

Forget-me-not Myosotis

We think of the Forget-me-not as being an old English name, but in fact it was not used until the nineteenth century when it was popularised by the poet Coleridge. An old name for it was 'scorpion-grass'. Coleridge took the name from a German tale of a knight walking by a river with his love who asked him to pick some of the pretty blue flowers growing on the bank for her. In doing so he fell in, but managed to throw the flowers at her feet calling out 'Forget me not!' before he drowned. The annual garden forget-me-not that we know is a cross between the water and wood varieties but there are also alpine varieties and it grows widely across Europe and Asia. It is a small plant 8-10 inches high which becomes leggy in the last stages of flowering, bearing tiny bright blue flowers which can also be pink or white even on the same plant. It flowers in April and May and attracts several varieties of butterfly. It produces masses of tiny black seeds which germinate easily. The name myosotis means mouse ear, probably from the softness and shape of the leaves.

As a flower essence, Forget-me-not helps the mourning process and a broken heart. It allows the possibility of making contact on a spiritual level with someone who has died, giving people the opportunity to deal with pain and grief. It can also be very useful to those who have never fully resolved isolation and abandonment issues after the death of an important family member or friend during childhood. It can give comfort through dreams by opening direct or indirect contact with beings in another dimension, allowing us to realise our true, immortal, spiritual human nature. It can enable us to go into past lives and retrieve soul aspects lost through pain and unresolved issues. It gives awareness of our karmic connections in personal relationships and with those in the spirit world. It helps people who feel lonely and isolated and who feel no spiritual connection with others. It is useful in old age.

CHAKRAS

The Base Chakra: focuses and earths.

Emphasis on the Sacral Chakra in children because they have to function from the Sacral Centre because they have no Base.

A complete block in the functioning of the Throat Chakra.

Affinity for the Throat and Sacral Centres.

A remedy for the Brow Centre.

For a blocked Crown, so although the spiritual contact is there, it is muffled, so people have potential to be like stars but they can't realise it.

DREAMINESS

Great dreaminess, withdrawn, great difficulty staying here, dreaming detachment.

Poor concentration. People who would rather dream. Drifting away.

There is a detachment, a distancing, not being quite here. People quite distant from the practicalities of life. Cannabis users.

Great sleepiness, just want to go to sleep.

As if in a dream and the opposite - manic.

Can't find words. Dreamy, have to search for words and cannot remember and assimilate. A cotton wool kind of state in the head.

CHILDREN

A brilliant remedy for children. Helps them find truth within themselves.

Children who are shy and hide.

For small children: toddlers. Similar to Silica, not thriving, but more confident and outgoing than Silica, sociable, very active, hyperactive even.

For little girls who are sweet and endearing, too sweet and too aware of how to get attention. Very lively and active. As if this sweetness covers up the damage underneath.

Vaccine damaged children: particularly autism, attention deficit disorder, hyperactivity, bad eyesight, destructive behaviour. Affinity with the Thymus.

Children damaged by medication.

For children who cannot think, are slow in mental development.

Children who have nightmares.

PEOPLE WILLINGLY BURDENED

Gives a respite from that which has to be borne and cannot be avoided. For burdens which people want to carry willingly but find heavy, like the burden that children are for parents, and later that elderly parents are for their children. Also the burden of patients.

Brings back determination where it has been lost in those who work hard, especially mothers of young children who feel bowed down by the demands of young families and have little sense of self as a result. Mothers who feel penned, walled in. Remedy helps to give a sense of freedom and acceptance of the circumstances that are with her now.

Parents who are struggling with the pressures of life. Mothers and fathers raising children, taking on too much through fear, insecurity or necessity.

REVEALS PAST TRAUMA

A remedy that goes deep into the karmic past. It releases abuse from previous lives. A child who is a little Pulsatilla appears to change personality, as the remedy releases and exposes the syphilitic layer because the anger comes out, the desire to destroy and hurt from the pain that is released.

A remedy for people with recurrent sore throats and throat problems that do not respond because all the problems come from the past abuse and they cannot release the grief and pain.

FEMALE

A strong affinity with the female reproductive organs.

Sacral Chakra and infertility problems.

Puberty in girls and all the problems associated with periods beginning. Also with periods ending - the menopause.

An important remedy for menstrual problems. When the menses are absent and no ovulation is occurring in women who have had the pill - NBWS the pill. Dysmenorrhoea. Dysmenorrhoea at puberty.

Cysts. Cysts R ovary.

EMOTIONAL

Anxiety states and paranoia. Delusions being watched, persecuted. Fastidious. Agitated. Talkative. Very restless.

Does not like the limelight. Happy to be in other people's shadows.

Very emotional. Causeless weeping, choking, throat constriction.

Post natal depression.

Remedy can bring enormous peace and tranquility. Has soporific and sedative qualities.

Extremes covered by the remedy: hyperactivity, where the remedy will bring quietness and sedation and at the other end a dreamy, gooey state of inertia which can be energised by the remedy.

Can be helpful when people have lost a sense of themselves, feel downtrodden, have become dismissive and critical of other people, but there is a gentleness beneath this. A need to be acknowledged, to be seen but pressures and demands are such that they feel totally swamped.

GENERAL

A remedy of great sweetness in appearance, fragility underneath.

A strong affinity with radiation and especially radiation produced by appliances and particularly mobile phones. Victims of radiation.

It affects the pituitary and all processes of maturation connected with the pituitary.

Warm blooded. Cannot stand much heat.

Very thirsty - marked.

Very strong affinity for water.

Colds that begin with dry, sore throats like Aconite. Colds with non-specific symptoms.

Cerebral palsy - children who turn their heads to one side, can't keep head straight.

PHYSICAL

Head: terrible headache.

Ears: for earache in children especially R sided. Cancerous states of the ear and throat.

Throat: good for tonsillitis, ear problems, adenoids. Sore throats. Sinus pains and pain in throat.

Underfunctioning states of the thyroid particularly where the mentality is affected - slowness, loss of memory, inability to think, cretinism.

Urinary system: bloating through water retention. Water balance issues. Urinary problems. Genito-urinary tract and throat.

Extremities: intense, painful numbness and tingling all over, especially forearms.

Seep: insomnia.

MIASMS

A very tubercular remedy. Tubercular children.
Syphilitic stuff, blocked.

REMEDIES

Looks like Pulsatilla or Silica, fair and female. Like a thirsty Pulsatilla.
Tarantula. Bellis Perennis. Bay Leaf.
A strong relationship to Calc Carb and to Phosphorus.
Like Staphysagria for a sense of impotence and pain and anger, when
things are done to you that you cannot escape.

Frankincense
Boswellia sacra, carterii or thurifera

Frankincense has been prized for thousands of years as an ingredient of sacred incense. It was associated with prayers and burned on altars in Rome, Persia, Babylon and Assyria and was burned literally by the ton on special occasions.

Frankincense is a sweet smelling gum resin derived from Boswellia trees (sacra, carterii and thurifera are all names for the same tree) originally growing in Yemen, Oman, Eritrea and Somalian regions and now found throughout the East. The frankincense trade was at its height during the days of the Roman Empire when the resin was considered as valuable as gems or precious metals. It was burnt in huge quantities at festivals, marriages and deaths.

Frankincense is the purest incense. When burned it produces a white smoke which symbolises the prayers and praises of the faithful ascending to heaven and the vibration to carry these prayers heavenward. Its centering aroma is said to slow the nervous system and promote feelings of calm and introspection. It has many spiritual associations. The mythical Phoenix was thought to build its funeral pyre out of frankincense and myrrh. Frankincense was one of the gifts of the Magi, fulfilling Isaiah's prophecy that gold and frankincense would be brought from the Gentiles to honor the heavenly king. Some say that it was presented to the Christ Child by Balthasar, the black king from Ethiopia or Saba, others that it was carried by Melchior, the Bright Lord with the Diamond. In Christianity and Judaism it has symbolised the gentleness and sweetness of the spirit and the body's impermanence, while myrrh represents the bitterness and the suffering of incarnation.

In the Book of Proverbs, frankincense is described mixed with wine and myrrh to create a 'strong drink' to ease the pains of the dying, the bitter, and the condemned and it was used by the ancient Egyptians as part of the embalming process. It has also been used for thousands of years in perfumes and cosmetics. In China, frankincense was used as a treatment for leprosy and Pliny recommended it as an antidote to poison. The oil helps to improve dry, chapped skin and is also useful for the respiratory system during seasonal changes. It contains monoterpene compounds which give the oil astringent, antiseptic and anti-inflammatory properties.

ESOTERIC

This remedy was a gift to the Christ child at the beginning of the Age of Pisces. A gift of Christ-centred consciousness and the awakening of such. This consciousness is now ready to change and this remedy can help it change greatly, by changing the consciousness of nations.

It will surround you with the source of the Christ light and enhance your healing properties nine-fold. The number nine is symbolic here.

It helps you to understand how to worship and the true meaning of the word. How to break through the barriers which prevent you from worshipping and surrendering completely. Worship done in a none-egotistical way in harmony, brotherhood, light.

It enables a soul to contact once more the presence of God and therefore brings greater clear-sightedness and quietness of the mind.

Will help lift people up to renew a lost contact with the God force, the angelic realms.

It brings us liberation and fulfills our earthly purpose. It helps us to be more aware of the patterns which hold us back from fulfilling that purpose.

It purifies the being and removes bad thoughts and thought patterns from the subconscious and bad thought forms which attach themselves to the psyche over incarnations. It will bring a state of reverence and harmony.

It gives us time for solitude and inner reflection and an introspective harmonisation with our beautiful selves.

The remedy can bring new help. You ask, we listen. You must call upon us more than you do.

Links greatly to the constellation of stars, the groups rather than the individual stars.

Connects with star energy which is love, so much love.

Corresponds to the angelic energies surrounding the planet at midwinter which are at their most potent and powerful.

Its energy is purple and gold. Its light is green. Red is the colour of the power it brings once you have learned to relax. It has the pure vibration of gold, the true vibration of the father and Christ energy.

CHAKRAS

Opens and expands the Heart Centre.

Heals the deep wounds most people have within the Heart.

Frankincense

Can put you back in touch with your Heart Centre and Heart values.

It awakens the seeds of love and wisdom and peace within the Heart Centre and joins men together with this harmony so that nations realise working together is ultimately the best way of understanding God's truth.

Awakens consciousness. It rekindles the Christ light in the heart with love and harmony and peace and light.

It wakens the mind in the heart and the heart in the head.

Safely enhances the opening of the now evolving Upper Brow in those who are ready.

Brings divine grace, the opening of the Upper Heart. Without this act of grace nothing is possible.

It affects the Brow Centre and harmonises between the Upper Heart and Brow.

It will help to clear the Throat Chakra.

A remedy for the upper Centres: Heart, Thymus and Throat.

Affinity with Crown Centre and upper bodies.

CLEARING THE PAST

For souls who have sacrificed themselves in previous lives - this is the Christ Energy. Those who have given themselves to God. The trauma can be so great they can't recognise they gave their souls to God in previous lives.

It helps to remove in a very deep and profound way the effects that are still playing within us from past lives.

For any situation where the person is nearly drowned or has drowned in a past life.

ANCIENT WISDOM

Enables you to open many doors of ancient knowledge and healing and puts you in state of harmony and humility and peace so you can use the information correctly. It can open many doors: karmic, ancestral and the doors of ancient, ancient civilisations, the knowledge of which has been locked away, for humanity has travelled so far in the wrong direction. Now the turning point is near for so many souls are opening themselves to the light this information can again be received.

It facilitates entrance into ancient temples but you can only enter in complete humility with the heart truly open, bearing no grudges or resentments toward any soul past, present or future.

Its power is that of initiation and it allows you to act and speak appropriately.

This is an energy of great diffusion, a loss of concentration, a loss of memory and focus and it is within that state that great knowledge is received, observed, used and channelled without ever being grasped by the conscious mind. It is a positive state of confusion and diffusion.

LIGHT OUT OF DARKNESS

Linked greatly to the darkness, but the peace, safety and the solace within the darkness with the shining of the golden lantern to light your way.

The still point in the turning world. The still point at which the light shines out of the darkness.

This is the point of manifestation when the light of the spirit is born in earthly matter. This is also a point of completion as well as a point where the old is left behind and the darkness of matter is abandoned and the body of light is taken on.

This remedy takes you to the core of your being, to the point of darkness where all feels lost, to the dark night of the soul. Then it brings you out again into the light. A remedy of Pluto, Hades, Persephone.

In its energy is the need to plummet to the depths, to go into suffering in order to find the still point and the great light that awaits.

In the darkest hour it brings peace and hope when all is lost. When all has been or is about to be taken away, this is the remedy.

Remedy for people at the end of their tether, suicidal. Can't see the light. Great trauma and tragedy, remedy helps guide them through.

It will help you to go where you have to go spiritually. When you cannot see the end and you have to trust.

Where it is like going into dark tunnel and cannot see the light at the end this will give trust, faith, hope and certain knowledge that all will be well and the light will return.

STRESS & RELAXATION

It can help you relax to the core of your being. Breaks down barriers of stress and negative protection that you have built up over not only this life, but many lifetimes.

It purifies, energises and teaches you to relax, which none of you really understands properly.

Stress that people don't know how to deal with.

Frankincense

People who are very low, irritable, depressed, sad and grumpy, especially at Christmas, for whatever reason.

Calms those in distress. Brings courage to those worn down by long years of caring and hardship.

Linked to the depths of water and the turbulence of the emotional body especially where there is conflict, great anguish in the soul.

CONTROL

It is a remedy which releases control.

It is for situations in which we have no control or which we are trying to control. It takes away the control and allows the greater guidance to come through.

It is a useful remedy for any situation where we are trying to control or hold on so it can be very useful at the end of life or during a birthing process.

Brings release, opening up.

PEACE

Creates a state within of calmness and great peace.

Can restore quietness and peace to a disrupted heart and soul.

Brings deep peace and harmony.

Helps the soul resolve its dilemmas.

The remedy brings great tranquillity, calms the troubled mind, bringing peace and understanding.

There is no fear. At the core will be peace, the creative dance, which is itself peace. Peace is the earth from which grows the flower of love. Be still and know that thou art God.

Each soul has its own burden to carry and the remedy helps you to face any difficult situation with calm, grace and humility.

It will remove fear and anxiety from the aura and help you to overcome any ordeal on whatever level you are faced with it.

Brings quietness and resolution where there is turbulence on any level, including the physical.

Good remedy for sleeplessness, especially if it is caused by too many worries and anxieties. You cannot switch off, still the mind.

Deep, peaceful sleep and it was as if the stress and anxiety just oozed out of me.

FUN

Brings fun and laughter.

A remedy for the inner child, releasing the joy of playfulness and a childlike sense of wonder that we lose as we grow older.

It is also useful for children who are too serious or whose circumstances in this life prevent them from enjoying their childhood.

Babies who don't want to be here.

HUMILITY

It will help you all to understand your own truth and to come into your own power without ego.

Gives people greater humility through increased consciousness and awareness.

Helps souls who are almost too humble, quiet and accepting, who withdraw their emotions, demands and voice into too quiet a place for the turbulence of the emotions of the situation around them.

GIVING

Within this stillness there is great abundance. Links us into this abundance and endless giving, giving.

Very much about giving from a place where we are not depleted. To give and not to count the cost.

DYING

An excellent remedy for old age and for a fear of dying. There should be no fear, there should be joy and a vision of the light.

For anyone dying and for evolved souls when they are dying. It will allow distractions to fall away and for the soul to go straight into the light and to pass without hindrance.

It allows the soul lessons of the incarnation to be taken forward at the point of death, for there to be consciousness.

It can be left with the dying person and they will use its energy when they need it.

It will enable the consciousness of evolved souls to be gathered together in the light even through surgery and drugs. It can be taped onto the Heart Centre.

Frankincense

GENERAL

Good for people in prison situations or for any incarceration.

Animals are helped by this remedy.

It has a cleansing and purifying effect, spiritually, emotionally and physically. As if the spirit is bathed in the water of life and energised and refreshed.

PHYSICAL

Head: stress headaches. Sensation as if the head was compressed.

Stiff neck and tense shoulders < L

Mouth: L sided ulcer eruption on roof of mouth. Mouth ulcers.

Teeth sensitive L upper.

Nose: tickling in nostril; desire to sneeze.

Throat: thick black tar sensation around.

Heart & lungs: pathology, asthma, cardiac arrest.

Stomach: great for digestive disturbances of any sort.

For the pneumo-gastric nerve.

Blood: blood disorders, heart pathology, AIDS

Nervous system: calms the nervous system and enhances states of being free from tension and separation.

For injuries that have caused brain damage.

Useful in MS.

Where limbs or fingers have been severed.

R sided paralysis of the face.

Pins and needles in L foot.

CONNECTIONS

Images of destruction and natural disasters. This will help through the chaos and give peace and strength.

Will be much needed in the future in decades to come when it will seem to many there is no light, no future only darkness.

REMEDIES

Use with Amethyst and Lapis Lazuli.

Strong connection with Rose and Lotus and can be used with great effect in combination with them.

PRESCRIBING NOTES

Restores order where there has been chaos. Clears a confusing picture where you do not know where to begin.

Do not give to people not ready for it, if they are stuck in the material world, as it is too powerful.

Hazel Coryllus avellana

H azel was on of the first trees to recolonise Britain after the Ice Age, coming soon after the Birch. It is a small tree, usually a large shrub as it tends to self coppice, throwing up new shoots from the base as branches break off. Hazel poles have been useful because of their suppleness and ability to split and bend, so they have been used as the framework for early dwellings and for coracles, as well as for hoops and baskets. Hazels grow well near water and hazel twigs are the favourite of water diviners. The catkins are a welcome sight in late winter and the nuts are a rich source of food for wildlife and, in the past, for people. The hazel was important to the Celts, particularly the Irish, symbolising wisdom. It was linked to the salmon, who eat the nuts when they fall into the water. It was believed that a salmon which had feasted on hazelnuts was full of knowledge and that eating the fish gave farsight or clairvoyance. The energy around a hazel bush is described as being silvery and quick moving, and the tree has also been associated with Mercury or Hermes. It is said that meditating under a hazel tree brings the spirit alive and allows you to cast off the old and bring in the new. The Celtic god of love carried a hazel staff, as did early pilgrims - Hazel was believed to give protection.

ESOTERIC

This is a remedy of the most powerful energy of gentleness. It has great protection, great warmth and powerful gentle energy. It brings a state of grace. A very gentle resting place.

It creates a protection of pure green energy, balancing, calming, healing. Its essence has a golden aura.

The effect of this remedy is like taking the sacraments and reinitiating yourselves into this present incarnation. It will bring you back to a central point after you have been thrown out of equilibrium by the diversity of energies that are around you all on your level and the energies of patients. It restores and rejuvenates, brings balance in the being.

It can make you aware of that which you have dealt with in previous incarnations, reaffirm your strengths and weaknesses, therefore has a very individual effect constitutionally.

It has a great effect on protecting the aura on all levels, brings much strength, gentleness and wisdom.

Its effects are very profound. You will find a heightened intuition and reception and a heightening in your healing energies. You will be aware of feeling energies unblock.

Much purification occurs under the branches of this remedy.

It works well on emotional bodies of adolescents as they move through puberty and helps them to see and understand. It a very protective remedy for children

Brings great magic, power, protection and can be used for any type of divination. Through its gates evil cannot penetrate. It was used by ancient Druids in many magical spells. Many of the great masters on your level when incarnate, used this remedy, not in homeopathy, but physical form. It holds renewal of faith and much protection.

CHAKRAS

Its healing energy works on all the Centres, the centre of each Chakra.

It brings sudden light and clarity and illuminates and stimulates the Base Centre.

Opens and connects the Base, Heart and Throat Chakras. Links the Base, Heart and Crown.

Disruption of Heart energy and this manifests in people whose actions and thoughts are very slow, without direction and thought and they wander aimlessly .

Connects the Head, the Base and the Heart ckakras.

Strong connection with the pituitary, Upper Brow Centre and Crown Centre.

Helps the Ida and Pingala to come together in the Brow: the mystic marriage.

ENERGY

A powerful remedy for all states of debility and exhaustion from whatever cause: mental, emotional, physical or from spiritual bombardment. It is a great remedy for your time now when all levels of the psyche can come under attack.

Low chronic energy states; not felt right for a long time; dragging themselves on through life.

One of most powerful remedies to induce a good sleep and a sleep which can take you close to other realms and give visions of other worlds and visions of past lives. This may be done by using potencies above 1m and not repeating too often.

Sleepy. Restless and fidgety, not sleepy. Energy is difficult. It is like walking through mud.

Feel drained on the left side.

Hazel

RELEASE

Can reconnect the person with the earth, themselves, their bodies and God.

Links with the earth, vibrations of soil and rock. For those who are linked with the earth in a negative way, where they cannot see the light of God within the earth. It links strongly with the negative karma held within the earth.

Enables those trapped in darkness to see the light. Frees souls trapped between worlds living in twilight. Releases those who haunt and possess. After exorcism.

For those who are vulnerable to earthbound spirits attaching themselves to them, feeding off their energy, not letting them die or leaving them in peace. Protection against dark forces.

Releases light within the being, allows the light to be manifest in the universe. Particularly it will allow those who are in contact with the light to bring it through.

Opens the door so rescues can happen easily. Although many may be traumatised, they go through with very little trauma. Remedy creates heart centred protection which allows that to happen.

MOVEMENT FORWARD

Puts people in touch with what they should be doing and gives them the strength of purpose and conviction to carry it through.

Gives the opportunity to go forward into the new, to take the crown of light, to leave what is known and familiar, to raise the vibration and to live in the light.

Gives the security to explore new realms. Releases creative potential. Frees from fear.

Gives the clarity and confidence to make the right choices.

Allows reconnection with the strength and knowledge of previous lives.

It is for all those striving to leave a past situation, to change and move on but who are rather stuck. It lifts us up above the emotion of the past.

Brings a very wide vision and helps us to become clearer channels of the light.

It is an energy of total and complete acceptance, with no judgement, criticism, shoulds or oughts and enables movement forward no matter how long they have been stuck.

LOSS OF FLUIDS

Has a most powerful effect on the fluids of the body, therefore will work on all emotional blocks and traumas. It gently works on rebalancing emotional traumas, the heavy effects of which have blocked the soul from its light and from God's light. It works gently and powerfully restoring the soul to harmony.

Will help kidneys to release fluid. Also good for debilitating diarrhoea and heavy menses - will slow down the flow and bring energy back into the being.

Will help mothers who have nursed too long and bodily fluids are becoming drained, hence they become exhausted and lose their centre. Remedy will not only help exhaustion and fluid balance but will help the infant to release and stop feeding if time is right.

Lessens all forms of catarrh in the body. Will calm a haemorrhage from any area.

MENTAL

Has an important effect upon the brain and mind, bringing new areas into being. Calms electrical effects on the brain and mind, can unscramble this activity and bring the higher centres back to peace.

It helps to still the mind that constantly gives a commentary. It would be useful in schizophrenia.

EMOTIONAL

For those who need nurturing, gentleness, who cannot stand strong reactions to things or remedies, who cannot take strong advice. They need understanding and patience.

For those who have been stultified and trapped by criticism, who bear the pain in their hearts from always having been found fault with. Those who feel they can never be right and who doubt themselves. This will put them in touch with their own inner strength.

The remedy brings up the emotions from the memory. Allows remembering and reconnecting.

Those who feel burdened, in pain, switched off and don't feel or respond any longer, there is no emotional energy or support to give any longer. Isolated and disconnected from their source and all others around them.

Hazel

A slow aimless restlessness where the person cannot find peace in sleep, work or distraction or even in the thought of death or suicide, so therefore they are suspended.

Gives strength, perseverance and resilience.

For children who are undergoing more and more pressures in school.

It can heal the mischievous spirit in children and adults who are very insecure.

It will help the broken heart. Can be given to all those suffering sadness, bereavement, separation, rejection, humiliation, unworthiness, cruelty. To rekindle the spark crushed in so many by the hard workplace, the rat race of ambition and competition.

Lot of anger and self-righteousness. Anger borne out of indignation, space being invaded.

Panic attacks. Calms fear generally. Profound effect on the adrenals: calms them, prevents the surges of adrenalin that cause fear and panic.

Protection. Those over-protected.

GENERAL

Depressive states of mind, body and energy.

SAD and the effects of a lack of physical light.

Lack of reaction in the nervous system. Where someone appears to be unaffected and does not react to any stimuli, but they wander around with no direction and little joy.

A remedy for all healers to enhance healing power. Can be used at the beginning of healing sessions.

Cleansing remedy. A very protective remedy.

Mistreated animals.

Has many physical symptoms. A lot of physical pathology.

Excellent for pain in any sphere. An easer of pain on every level.

Can heal negative pockets of energy, e.g. fistula, diverticular disease and so on.

Affinity with the skeletal and muscular structure. Can help to realign our spinal energies.

Sharp pains. Pains on the right side.

PHYSICAL

Eyes: stinging badly. Itching L eye extending to armpit.

Mouth: paralysed, can't speak.

Throat: for problems of the thyroid and parathyroid glands. Tightening in the throat and chest.

Lungs: for problems with breathing, especially in men.

Female: helps in all states of menstrual trauma especially with effects of Pill and HRT.

Of great use in menopausal years to keep balance.

Will often help heaviness and disorientation felt during months of pregnancy when mother is confused and unsure - will bring back light into her aura and emotionally rebalance her.

Excellent for labour pains, especially when they manifest in the back.

Stomach: pains in. Nausea.

Intestines: profound effect on the intestine, calming diarrhoea or loosening constipation.

Diarrhoea before normal stool.

Pancreas: rebalances blood sugar, whether too much or too little in the blood.

Extremities: sudden excruciating pain L hip. Discomfort L hip. R hip as if sprained. R knee. R shoulder. Pain shins. L hand heavy and cold, as if dismembered.

CONNECTIONS

With the pituitary and Sycamore Seed.

It has the effect of silver light.

Indirectly connected to a crystal skull.

MIASMS

Syphilitic side to the remedy.

REMEDIES

It is a missing link in a chain of remedies which will come clear later.

Has a great affinity with Silverfish in its ancient powers and connotations.

Would work well with Moonstone in exorcism. May be given to the patient once the exorcism has taken place to close aura quickly, but not before. Moonstone will draw out the entity and this will protect afterwards.

Linked to Ayahuasca: energy going both upward and downward not spiralling like Ayahuasca.

Sepia. Hornbeam. Elm. Ash. Yew. Amethyst. Emerald. Green.

PRESCRIBING NOTES

Can be given alongside Calc Carb, perhaps as an LM.

Can be used serially in conjunction with crystals and colours, to restore integrity and discipline to each of the chakras. It is as if each chakra can be given a cleansing by this remedy.

It can be used to enhance the direction of any remedy, to take that remedy to the core of the problem. It heals and refines.

Can bring on some very acute symptoms that will come and go quickly as blocked energy areas heal and purify. Do not interfere with these effects. These will go of their own accord.

Can be a physical evacuation as a result of the cleansing of the Centres after this remedy.

Himalayan Blue Poppy
Meconopsis betonicifolia

The Himalayan Blue Poppy is one of the meconopsis family which features 45 species of short-lived, hardy perennials, naturally found in moist, shady mountainous areas of the Himalayas, Burma and China with one species being found in Western Europe. The blue poppy is the National Flower of Bhutan and used to be found in such profusion in South East Tibet that it was known as the 'Land of the Blue Poppy'. In its natural habitat it is now an endangered plant growing on the edges of yak pastures. It can grow up to 2 ft high, the stems each having 4-5 delicate, cupped flowers which are 3-5 inches wide and bloom in early summer. The flowers are sky-blue in colour unless the soil is alkaline (in which case they are wine purple). It needs cool, rainy summers to grow.

The roots contain narcotic principles and the plant is used in Tibetan medicine as an analgesic, in healing broken bones and in the treatment of inflammation from fractures. The Blue Himalayan Poppy was introduced into England in the 1930s where it grows best in cool damp summers.

As a flower essence it represents the essence of spiritual lineage. It helps us to fulfill our potential in this lifetime, and to build on strengths gained in the past. It furthers insight and psychic skills.

ESOTERIC

Intimately connected with the essence of conception: of the individual, of the holy spirit upon the earth, of the immaculate conception between the pineal and the pituitary. It relates to the seed of the Divine form within the human.

It is about the birth and death cycle, knowing but not knowing.

It is a harbinger of the dawn of enlightenment.

Restores trust and hope.

It comes with a very powerful force field of etheric light that opens a window to where we are going, It binds us together individually and collectively to the reality that nature is a condensation of light and that the spirits of nature play in this ocean of light.

It is a remedy of great protection and creates around the aura such a strong safe haven it is difficult for spirits unlike itself to come in.

It is linked to the power that can refine and spiritualise us.

The remedy is capable of bringing great gratitude and joy to the heart, allowing change to be initiated, bringing to consciousness our illusions then giving the determination to let them go.

Himalayan Blue Poppy

HEART OPENING

A Heart centred remedy. Opens the Heart chakra and the upper chakras.

Initiates the Heart Chakra to open. Waters the seed of life which lies within the heart and awakens real contact with God.

Will remove bitterness, resentment and fear from the heart and will awaken true life again.

Brings great warmth and healing to Heart and Upper Heart, restoring faith in God and trust in life.

SELF-LOVE

Clears self-sabotage and self-hatred and their cause which lies in a lack of trust and faith and in the illusion that we are separate from God.

Reminds us that we cannot worship God and hate ourselves nor put ourselves down or turn against ourselves in any way.

For people who hide their light and are afraid of showing it. For those who have been taught or conditioned not to be who they are, where there are inner seekings but they have been implanted with beliefs that they can't fulfill them.

For people who feel they have lost the connection with the light.

Brings the peace and strong protection of the light and restores a sense of confidence and self-esteem. Allows us to be direct and strong.

Restores pride, self esteem and confidence and enjoyment to those on the spiritual path.

Brings a connection to others and a sense of wholeness of the self, especially with relation to the body.

UNITY

Within this remedy lies the knowledge and the experience of our unity.

There is great well-being and a sense of integration.

For people who need to integrate back into humanity and into a sense of the common good and common experience, For those who feel isolated and different from everyone else. For those who have lost the connection with other people and think no-one can help them.

For those who have lost contact with God and are suffering from it.

For a twin who has lost their twin and suffers from that loss in some way.

For people who don't feel whole.

It brings us back to the state of unity. Within that unity we all have all the power we need to heal ourselves of any condition, because any condition other than light is one of illusion.

PERSEVERANCE FURTHERS

The remedy gives perseverance and endurance and enables us to keep on trying and to keep growing.

Gives the patience and tenacity to stay with it, to hang on in there when the tendency is to run, to stand firm in a difficult situation.

FEAR

Calms deep fear.

Fainting from fear and fright.

Great deep fear to the point of panic turning against oneself as in suicide.

SHOCK

The remedy will strengthen purpose by removing deep, unresolved shock and trauma from wherever it lies within the aura.

For those who do not know where they have been as a result of deep old shock. They will see, breathe and feel true love.

A sense of being in limbo, unable to move through a dark place, not wanting to go alone.

Not being able to retrieve knowledge because of trauma. This will help release the trauma and help clear the way to get the cycle going, moving, interconnecting.

HIDING

For when people get stuck, lack any movement, where there is hiding instead of sharing and getting on.

For people who have had to hide their light for fear of oppression.

Children in school who are bullied and have to hide their light to be one of the gang.

THE ELDERLY

An important remedy for the elderly.

Where the life force is weak.

For the dying. For terminal pain which is better for weeping.

For collapse in every sense.

Osteoporosis.

Himalayan Blue Poppy

GENERAL

Lack of energy.

Extreme coldness.

Severe pain which is much better for crying.

Fidgety.

Delusions of rats and mice.

Inflammatory states, especially glandular swellings, TB.

A great remedy for AIDS.

PHYSICAL

Neck: stiffness of the neck > stretching the chin up.

Shoulders: great pain across the shoulders.

Female: stabbing pains L breast. Tender breasts

For women after a hysterectomy, when they feel they have lost their womanhood and don't know who they are anymore in relation to society.

Nerves: for severed fingertips - helps the nerves to heal. Where limbs have been lost.

Cerebral palsy.

Tumours: for tumours growing on their own without regard for the rest of the body.

Where growth is misplaced or stunted.

For lumps and cysts especially when the person feels they are alien to them and that their body is not their own. There may be a history of cutting them off and not looking for the deeper pattern.

Extremities: swelling of L foot and ankle.

Very cold legs.

Skin: eruptions

CONNECTIONS

With the first atomic explosion.

Colours green, gold, lilac and purple.

MIASMS

Very psoric and tubercular.

PRESCRIBING NOTES

This remedy has an enormous sphere of action and unblocks. When remedies don't work this remedy will help those truly indicated to do their job.

Works very quickly and deeply.

The remedy can be sent through prayer.

Holly Berry   Ilex aquifolium berry

T*he berries for this remedy were collected in January. The berries grow only on the female trees although holly itself is usually considered to have masculine energy. Holly leaves and berries are an age-old fertility symbol and a charm against witchcraft and black magic. Holly berries have been connected through the tree with the midwinter solstice and then with Christmas for hundreds if not thousands of years. They were linked to the fiery red of the sun god, who was reborn at the winter solstice. Later the red berries came to symbolise the blood that was shed by Christ for humanity's redemption and the prickly leaves with the crown of thorns. The holly tree has long been considered to 'wear the Crown' and to be an important tree of magic and protection. Many people still consider it bad luck to fell a holly. The berries are poisonous to all except birds, causing diarrhoea and vomiting and so people have had no practical use for them apart from their decorative value.*

ESOTERIC

This berry, which has lasted all winter, and therefore has much knowledge, wisdom and strength. It has a direct link with the akashic records, to the lords of karma.

There is a great dichotomy with this remedy, a pull to the heavens and a pull down into the depths of great darkness.

It uses the energy of Saturn and of Chiron, and links to a new planet yet to come into human consciousness which has a direct link with Jupiter and Mercury. This planet, the remedy and this consciousness are linked to the Upper Brow Chakra.

It unleashes not only ancestors but collective sins of countries and continents, particularly areas of the sea where continents have sunk. It connects very much with past cycles of civilisations; the beginnings and endings of civilisations where there was great destruction in order that a new energy and vibration could come into manifestation on the physical and spiritual levels.

Remedy will help us absorb more knowledge and information on the kabbala, the tree of life.

Gives peace and acceptance, brings down higher knowledge into our lives without any conflict. Very strongly protective. It is a balance and a refuge.

Enables us to live out the truth, accepting the vicissitudes of life without struggling and gives the understanding that it all needs to happen for our own good and the good of mankind.

Promotes connection and communication. A doorway that opens to other worlds, other dimensions.

CHAKRAS
Thymus Chakra. Heart Chakra. Sacral Chakra.

BLOOD
Remedy symbolises blood taken from us all as blood brothers and increases our Heart Centre connection.

It has a big connection with the blood and the whole circulatory system and heart.

A remedy par excellence for dealing with the ill effects of blood transfusions. May often have to be used with X ray as much blood is irradiated.

It represents the blood of all ages, the bleeding of the earth and it combines with the power of the serpent. Much blood has been spilt over the ages, much blood sacrifice. All this is still in the collective memory and still needs to be cleared and healed.

An image for this remedy is the crown of thorns on the forehead of Jesus. The cruelty, persecution, violence, injustice, pain and suffering imposed by the ignorance of humanity is transformed by the release of love, represented by the blood.

People who have witnessed blood letting, accidents, violence and those who deal with it: the police, paramedics.

Violent impulses, desire to see blood, so syphilitic.

CONFRONTING & RELEASING DARKNESS
Major use of this remedy is that it can fight dark black magic power, but needs to be taken by the individual who is confronting the forces. Keeps you calm, tranquil, fearless and peaceful within the heart to enable you to fight off all evil forces and to make you recognise these forces so that you will see them. They will not be able to hide from you if you take the remedy.

It has a two fold purpose: that of cleansing and purifying but also releasing and unleashing negative energy and patterns in the individual within a group, family, society and within the collective.

STRENGTH IN ADVERSITY

Is very useful for initiates who are going through many trials and tribulations. Will give you strength to fight off the negative forces which come at you all now. In all times of enormous stress where you feel completely unable to cope or give way to negative emotions within you, take the remedy three times weekly, in a 30th potency, for no longer than three weeks at any time. It will keep you calm and centred and able to deal with anything. It does this by keeping you in a place of peace and humility, with an open heart. Many will try to upset this balance. They will see your vulnerable points and try to get in but this remedy will keep you calm and providing you keep calm and work in humility, you will be able to face any turmoil.

Where there's a desire to run away from life and all that plagues us.

LACK OF CONCENTRATION

No focus and does not want to concentrate, wants to go away and play, go into the dark. A quality of age.

Not knowing what to do, which direction, need for guidance. Total state of turmoil. Not knowing what you want.

For those easily led and misled. For gullibility, lack of discrimination, for changing without thought, without time to sit and contact the wisdom within.

Difficulties of concentration and issues around concentration and perseverance. Helps us to let go of striving and let higher wisdom take over. Helps us to trust that it will be there, trust our perceptiveness rather than our effort.

Thoughts come and go in the mind but so fast, there is so much brain activity you cannot focus. Very scattered.

Thoughts and sensations sliding out of reach. Cannot bring the mind into focus.

VIOLENCE

For people like the survivors at Dunblane, those who have witnessed great horror in this life or a past incarnation or were party to or a victim of a mass killing. A remedy for both the perpetrators and the victims.

Closely associated with dying in a traumatic fashion, often at the hand of somebody else, including situations where you turn your hand on yourself.

The darkness is almost unbearable. They go mad to escape it, do anything to escape it. Feel very trapped. Violent anger, violent impulses.

Communities doing violence to their own people which leaves a painful and strong imprint on the collective memory.

PREGNANCY, BIRTH & DEATH

Works well on all children and children in the womb. Balances the four elements creating harmony within the soul.

Good for anything to do with pregnancy and birth. Puts children within the Christ Light and the spirit of Love. Universal brotherhood and love helps to balance the four elements within the being, especially tiny beings, who are innocent and pure.

The remedy is of great importance to help the incarnating soul at birth and later where there has been vaccination. It helps the mother to form a link with the baby.

For babies who come in too quickly and are a bit shocked by it, a bit blue around the lips.

Haemorrhaging in childbirth.

It helps the disincarnating soul at the end of their stay here. Helps them to leave. Helps the silver thread to be withdrawn.

EMOTIONAL

Utter, absolute despair. Pain, suffering. Separated. Forsaken. Contraction.

Not wanting any more pain and suffering, impossible to take any more, experience any more and yet it continues.

People who need this remedy are in crisis. They have reached a point of no return, they must go on but it is as if they have reached a fork in the road. A remedy for decision and decision-making. A remedy for courage, for helping people to make up their minds and have courage to act in a situation.

Deep, deep aching pain in the heart. Great grief, unspoken dumb suffering, numbness.

Numbed or desolate in some way especially around the heart and the Heart Chakra. Those who have disconnected from their emotions.

Autism and similar cut off states, to draw those shut off souls into accepting life, to encourage them not to be cut off and frightened.

People who carry the weight of great guilt, who retreat into moral numbness. Guilty, blushing with guilt. Feeling as if they've been found out.

Unworthiness, not good enough, not deserving, guilt, shame, a need for cleansing.

In the end this remedy will bring great peace, but it can give bad aggravations, bring out things that are hidden, dark things people don't want to look at, but in the end it will release them.

Desire to run away and to escape, total unworthiness. Struggling with aspects of self that doesn't like.

A remedy for vengeful women. For jealousy - a big root of evil.

Suspicious. Irritable. Impatient. Intolerant.

For those who lack confidence, who are vague, scattered.

Very mischievous remedy. Shape shifting, deception. People with very manic energy. Destructive. Chaotic.

Great vulnerability with this remedy. For those needing protection.

GENERAL

Itchiness. Twitchings. Needle-like pricklings.

Great heat. Hot and itchy. Cannot stand heat.

One sided symptoms.

Cleanses the spine and all the centres and nervous system.

Connection with the lymph glands.

For surgery, especially under general anaesthetics, when the consciousness is withdrawn by drugs.

Alcoholism.

PHYSICAL

Head: intense pain round the head with nausea and numbness. Pain on R side of head.

Neck: R sided pain neck and shoulder. Neck seized up.

Face: sensation of paralysis in right cheek.

Eyes: gritty. Sticking pain in eye. Possible pathology.

Mouth: numbness under the tongue from the remedy, producing nausea in the throat.

Stomach: nausea. Nausea and vomiting for 36 hours from 1am after the proving.

Heart: all heart pathology. Palpitations. Erratic heart beat. All aspects of the circulation, the spleen, aching veins in legs etc.

Extremities: sharp pain in both axillae as if needle stuck in.

CONNECTIONS

Wars: especially Crimean, First World War, US Civil War.

A remedy for wars in the future involving the use of gases which break down cell structure causing bleeding. Connection with Iraq and the Arab states. Possibly a remedy for the Ebola virus.

Link between earth and water

MIASMS

Syphilitic: hiding, secret, deceitful energy.

REMEDIES

Copper Beech. Yew and Mistletoe, especially the berries. Plutonium.

Compare Raspberry and the naevus that looks like a raspberry.

PRESCRIBING NOTES

Remedy should only be used by initiates.

Two-fold use: as normal remedy picture, also used to fight powers of darkness - for this purpose must only be used by the initiate dealing with the problem. Will give her/him power to discriminate between what is light and what is dark. Dark forces will not be able to hide.

Can break down those barriers that people put up constantly and persistently in the process of their healing. This is a remedy a bit like crystal remedies which you can give if you suspect a patient of taking the indicated remedy but holding back on it. They will come back but they will have told you only partial success when you know they could have managed more.

Kigelia Africana Sausage Tree

Kigelia Africana (or Kigelia pinnata), belongs to the family Bignoniacea and is named after its grey-green, gourd-like fruits, which grow up to a metre in length and weigh as much as 10Kg. A fast growing tree, it reaches 23 metres or more in height. It is widespread across Africa and is found in wet savannah and river areas, where it occurs in abundance. It is semi-deciduous with grey-brown smooth bark and large, crisp leathery leaves which are browny red when young. The flowers are spectacular in both colour and form and are among the biggest of all indigenous flowers. The maroon, velvety petals are vividly veined a bright yellow. They are borne from August to October in long, dangling sprays of 5 - 12 flowers beneath the canopy. The fragrance of the flower is not pleasing to humans but attracts the dwarf epauletted bat (Micropteropus pusillus), its pollinator. The flowers do not remain on the tree for very long and as they drop, animals come to feed on the nectar-rich blooms: impala, duiker, baboons, bush pigs and lovebirds. The grey, sausage-shaped fruit has a thin skin covering a firm, fibrous fruit pulp containing numerous small, unwinged seeds. There is a dry bush joke that the worst place to camp is under a Sausage Tree - if the fruits don't crush you, then the elephants will as they come to collect the fruits. There is a widespread local belief that Kigelia fruits, when hung in your hut, will ward off whirlwinds. Dug-out canoes are made from the trunks and large roots.

Kigelia has a long history of medicinal use by rural African communities. Most commonly, traditional healers have used the Kigelia Tree to treat a wide range of skin ailments, from fungal infections, boils, psoriasis and eczema, through to the more serious diseases such as leprosy, syphilis and skin cancer. It also has internal applications, including the treatment of dysentery, ringworm, tapeworm, post-partum haemorrhaging, malaria, diabetes, pneumonia and toothache. The Tonga women of the Zambezi valley regularly apply cosmetic preparations of Kigelia fruit to their faces to ensure a blemish-free complexion. The fruit is a common ingredient in traditional beer, and is said to hasten the fermentation process. Perhaps not surprisingly, given its suggestive shape, the fruit has also found traditional use as an aphrodisiac.

The pods are kept as religious charms and fetishes and produce a red dye when boiled. Anecdotal evidence suggests that the tree has also been important in African shamanic practice and witchcraft.

A significant body of scientific literature confirms the validity of many of the traditional uses of Kigelia and suggests a number of new applications.

Several trials have supported the use of Kigelia fruit extract for treating skin cancer, and there is evidence that it is effective in the treatment of solar keratosis, skin cancer and Kaposi sarcoma. It is also marketed in Europe and the Far East as the active ingredient in skin tightening and breast firming formulations and in creams for eczema, psoriasis and sunscreening.

CHAKRAS

There is no Heart contact with those who need this remedy. Power but no love or warmth. They are frozen out of the Heart.

Brings warmth, energy in Heart area

Affects the hands in relation to the Heart Chakra.

Big effect on Throat Chakra.

Brow Chakra. Relates strongly to Crown.

For people who have misused the two centres in the head and the Heart Chakra and become very trapped because they can't control their body.

Energy of stars through Crown Chakra with power and light.

Energy brings grounding to those not earthed and lifts those too earthbound out of the material.

THROAT CHAKRA

A major Throat remedy.

Strongly suppressed throat energy.

Things bottled up and not said, producing chronic ache in throat.

Lack of vocal expression.

About expressing things with clarity so others can understand.

Deep sadness with focus at the throat.

It will help you speak your truth with dignity and to free the throat.

Desire to stretch so my throat can stretch. It wants to express something from way back.

Throat very sore, swallowing to prevent coughing. Pain L throat

Constriction in throat. Swollen R side. Mucous.

Aching muscles of throat and neck.

Tension in neck extending to shoulders. Can't move head back.

Back of neck rigid.

Brings great clarity and euphoria, with expression.

Kigelia

TRAPPED & STUCK

Stuck energy trapped in some way. Can't move out.

As if frozen in ice or amber or like a fossil - stuck in the past.

Brings people out of stuckness, brings them forward.

For those who lag behind, who have to catch up.

Feeling trapped on a mental and emotional level. Want to say things but can't make themselves understood. Feeling trapped inside, so desperate, no one understands, can't get emotions out.

As if after a stroke you can't make people understand what you want.

Very remote, very frightening, unable to verbalise.

Mentally ill, very ill. People on heavy psychiatric drugs.

Autism.

For souls trapped in a physical body, from diseases, accident, injury.

Those who are stuck in darkness through abuse of psychic powers and magic in the past.

Brings transformation.

GRIEF

The grief of regret, things not done, not said that should have been, not the grief of loss so much.

An awareness of what we have done wrong, mistakes we have made.

Grief at things that cannot be changed, linked to things that have to be endured. Where circumstances are such that we just have to get on with it.

Gives the ability to be like a mountain in the face of grief and tragedy and the realisation of what could have been different.

The remedy brings the sweetness of acceptance, and peace out of the pain.

A remedy to take people through really difficult times and give them a feeling of still water while they're in troubled water.

POSSESSION & CLEARING

Goes into the darkness more deeply than any other remedy.

Remedy opens channels for the most profound and deepest healing. Can release the darkest abominations of the soul and the planet.

This clearing needs doing. The more you work with the light the more darkness is revealed and healed. The brighter the light the more dark it illuminates. There is nothing to be afraid of but we have to deal with it.

Lot to do with possession. Possibly going on for a long time. It will clear old entities that have been trapped from incarnation to incarnation.

Enables the release of horrible dark energies which have been stuck and festering for aeons.

It taps into the darkest, nastiest aspects of the psyche and the soul. It connects with the most depraved levels of humanity.

The remedy can clear the deepest recesses of evil madness - people who are locked up in Broadmoor.

Relates to holocaust, genocide, to those who imprison others, torment them.

For those who court evil, consort with evil and play with demonic energy.

Also for those who have to deal with paedophiles and abusers, murderers, torturers. For those who try to help who themselves become damaged from contact with this energy. They come from the heart and compassion, but they are attracted to work in this area by their own karma and past activities so are vulnerable themselves.

Releases what is blocking the psyche and soul.

NERVOUS SYSTEM

Calms the nervous system.

For those who have no control over physical bodies. Where the body does not obey the will.

A lot of twitching.

Shaking all over, involuntary. Very restless types of chorea.

MS, nervous disorders, Parkinson's, Motor Neurone. St Vitus' Dance. Spasticity.

Paralysis of legs. Paralysis back of legs and spine, with coldness.

Paralysis in throat.

GENERAL

Connection with cancer. A lot of grey in the aura.

Immune system.

Allergies especially to animals; environmental and food allergies.

Kigelia

AIDS.

Splintering sensations.

Good for old injuries.

Coolness. Icy cold and shivering all over. Coldness R side.

Feeling hot and burning.

Muscle tension. Want to rub body, have a massage. Deep tension.

Twitchiness deep in body including internal organs, can feel them moving.

PHYSICAL

Head: sensations in top of head and eyes, ears.

Tight band of pain across forehead into back of neck.

A lot of stiffness in the back of the neck.

Tendency to fall over.

Ears: pains in ears. Earache R to L. Meniere's.

Nose: the common cold. L nostril and L eye very runny.

Face: lips dry and sore

Mouth: salivation

Neck & shoulders: neck very stiff, also shoulders. Very stiff, need to stretch.

Throbbing in ears and down neck

Heart: fluttery.

Stomach: feeling sick and dizzy. A very strong feeling of nausea.

Female: menstrual flooding. The possibility of a miscarriage. Both always with coldness.

Abdomen: diarrhoea. Pain L side, low down.

Back: as if a rod down spine and another across shoulders (< R side), forming a cross.

Extremities: arthritis. Pulsation in L ankle. Very painful feet. Really hurts to stand on them. Twitchy toes and fingers.

CONNECTIONS

Connected with Aborigines or people who know their history.

Connected to past, present and future.

Link with ginger.

Images and Symbols: Arctic, windswept, cold, ice, deep dark, huge
icebergs, hidden depths, groaning sounds. Ice containing fossils from
things gone before. Silver pickaxe.

Clouds. Trees entangled. Like a feather breaking down into fractals,
smaller and smaller, disintegrating. Big thick snake. Darkness, oil,
demons. Musical clef. Verbalising with love and Angelic tones you get
from music. The colour orange. Grey and silver. Big expanse of
greyness.

MIASMS
Syphilitic miasm. Very dark aspect to this remedy.

REMEDIES
Amber. Rose Quartz. Ayahuasca. Wych Elm. Syphilinum.

The Milky Way

The Milky Way is one of the estimated 140 billion galaxies in the universe, the spiral galaxy we can call home. Our sun is one of the estimated 100-400 billion stars which form it. With the average distance between stars estimated at 30 million million kilometres, the size and dimensions become incomprehensible. In the Milky Way alone, astronomers estimate that statistically there must be millions of planets hosting advanced civilisations.

The stars in the disc where our solar system resides are mainly young - between 1 million and 10 billion years old, those in the bulge at the centre, which contains an enormous black hole, are older - 10 billion years or more. The halo around the galaxy is composed mainly of dark matter with a low density of old stars gathered in clusters.

Astronomers believe that the galaxy formed out of a large, fairly spherical cloud of cold gas, rotating slowly in space. The cloud began to collapse in on itself, or condense. Initially, some stars may have formed as the gas cloud began to fragment around the edges, with each fragment condensing further to form a star or group of stars. As the cloud continued to collapse, more and more stars were formed. Since the cloud was rotating, the spherical shape began to flatten out into the disc shape it has now.

Galileo was the first person to see the Milky Way as individual stars when he viewed it through a telescope in 1609. Before this it had only been seen as a river or as heavenly smoke. Every culture has a myth to explain its presence. The oldest known reference to the Milky Way is that of the sacrifice of Utnapishtim, the Sumerian Noah, after the ark was stranded on Mount Ararat following the deluge. In Egypt when the goddess Isis fled to escape the monster Typhon, she threw stalks of grain behind her and these became the stars of the Milky Way. It was also said to have been formed by the body of the goddess Nut as she lay across the night sky. Classical Greek mythology describes the Milky Way as a smear of milk from either Hera the wife of Zeus or Rhea the Earth goddess. For the Australian aborigines it was the smoke of an ancient people's sacrifices; for the Chinese it was the heavenly river where the mothers of the sun and moon bathe their children before they enter the sky. For people everywhere the Milky Way has been seen as the path that souls take on their way to the afterlife.

This proving was done using two remedies, both encompassing the same energy. One was made using a clear quartz crystal pointing towards a bottle of ethanol on a moonless night at the Autumn equinox in 1995. The other was created through a meditative channelling of the energy of the Milky

Way into ethanol. The name Solarfish was given by the guide channelled through the groups. Neither of these essences was potentised for the proving and we have since been told that only the Milky Way remedy and not the channelled essence should be used in potency.

ESOTERIC

A rebirth, initiation.

Links you to planetary heart/soul consciousness, so energy not of an individual nature.

Balances masculine and feminine principles and brings soul consciousness in contact with the gods.

A keyword is illusion.

For those in the wrong body, the wrong incarnation; people who've reincarnated too quickly.

Important remedy for children - so many now being born have a high vibration already and they will come into this remedy well. It is a remedy of love, of healing for the heart, for when we love we will then produce universal peace.

Filters out negative vibration. Protects.

Transcends intellect. Anti-science and the need to explain everything which is part of the abyss.

Brings in heart knowledge not intellectual knowledge.

Related to the Central Pillar and the two upper triangles of the Cabbalistic Tree, so links spirit and soul consciousness with the Heart Chakra so that it can be used in the world.

CHAKRAS

Influences all Chakras, along the spine.

Expands the Heart, Throat, Crown.

Very much a Heart centred remedy, so it puts light back into people's lives and connection with other people.

Heart centred and links planetary group heart consciousness into the world.

It is on the same line from the Christ vibration but comes much expanded, fine, more subtle, able to bring greater awareness, greater aspects of joy, of sight, of true awareness through the Heart Chakra.

It is a vibration of the developed Heart Chakra, that will develop in the next century, that few souls yet manifest on this earth at this time.

Remedy sits in the Throat Chakra and helps us to talk to people with kindness and care, taking away the bitterness and spite.

Filters light through Crown to Third Eye and then Heart.

Remedy is the key to the Crown Chakra, to enable all the other remedies for it to work better and more effectively.

Unites two halves of brain, two aspects of Brow Chakra and pituitary.

LINK WITH THE DIVINE

Enables you to have a true connection with God.

It comes on a very high Heart vibration, it represents the greater love and energy beyond the Christ Vibration.

Its energy comes as yellow golden shimmering light, the dilution of the golden ray from the sun, from God

Link with Divine Light, essence of Love

Brings great purity, purity that is essential for us to find God.

Purity of Divine Solar Fire, that Solar Fire of which kundalini energy is but a dim echo.

Brings great expansion. It removes blocks, inhibitions to contacting Divine Love, to joy, to laughter.

The first step in being, listening to the gods. Like astral magic.

CONNECTION WITH THE UNIVERSE

Brings energy of suns beyond our solar system, level of vibration so fine we can barely comprehend it.

It is the start of greater awareness, greater communication between other solar systems, other worlds.

Enables the experience of universal and expansive energies.

Linked to the power of the infinite.

Allows us to have fun, to sing, to dance with the energy of the universe

Brings the awareness that we have the universe within us.

Brings unity and brotherhood, particularly between other worlds, other planets, other solar systems.

UNIFYING

Enhances greater brotherhood between people, heals relationships and heals particularly on the psychic and solar levels.

Symbolic of unity of humanity, brotherhood, sisterhood.

It is one with the silence, the harmonious unity of all things.
Unifying within the self.

THE ELEMENTS

This remedy goes to a point at which the four elements were created, a
  point before matter, of light. A point before expression, into
  nothingness which is everything.

It matches all the elements but especially wind and fire.

Connection with water and water element.

Carries light around the body.

REMEDY OF THE FUTURE

We are being prepared for the expansive energy of the future by this
  remedy.

A powerful, refined, purified energy that will only affect those who are
  evolved.

Such a high vibration that at this point (1995) not so many can attune to
  it, but it is important for connecting to the future or welcoming in the
  future and will be needed by more people as time goes on.

This is one of the first awarenesses of the vibration next to come, of
  which humanity will be conscious in the 21st century

CONNECTION & COMMUNICATION

Connection is one of the remedy's key words.

It helps us to realise again the strength of our connection with the earth,
  underneath our really strong connection with heaven, to walk, as
  Christ on the planet, with our feet on the earth and our heads and
  hearts to heaven.

Remedy gives peace, light and connection.

Connection between several things all at the same time or the connection
  between changing states.

Remedy will supply the balance needed to change from one balanced
  state to the next.

Increases the ability to take on aspects of divine teaching and express
  them in the world.

Connected with ability to radiate and magnetism - qualities of all healers
  and teachers.

Clears channels. Clears channels for meditation.

Enhances ability to channel in those who work from the Heart. Aids communication with beings of higher nature.

DESTRUCTION & TRANSFORMATION

Related to the vibration of destruction through tornado, volcano and radiation explosion. It will dilute these effects, make them harmless, transmute their energy into good to expand people's awareness and their capacity for love.

It brings great peace and harmony after and through destruction.

At the human level it represents destruction.

Good for people going through transformation where their lives are falling apart.

Family breakup, especially where one partner is not aware of the separation that will happen. For the children who are affected by these experiences. For the despair and shock within the family, sadness and grief of children especially, but also of the partners. Will bring peace and harmony enabling both partners to see the greater plan, to be aware of what they are being led through and why there has to be change.

It increases the wisdom and capacity for love and the capacity to receive love from the greater family of the world, of the solar system.

Allays fear, brings peace and harmony, makes safe a dangerous situation on any level, physically, mentally, psychically especially.

For those souls who may have turned inwards, are not aware of others, are too focussed on their own troubles, have cut themselves off from the vitality of life and who need to change.

For those who need to be moved on.

Paralysis, not necessarily physical, but emotional or mental where the person cannot make the connection to act as is appropriate to move on.

FOR THOSE NOT ON THEIR PATH

For those unable to make a choice, a commitment, in a quandary.

Uncertainty.

Sense of loss and confusion.

For those who are open, quick and perceptive, can see the conclusion of many things on earth before they have even started, but find it hard to connect with their own path.

Remedy enables people to connect with their heart and find their path.

Low boredom threshold and great dissatisfaction. Restlessness from a lack of satisfaction.

Start and stop many things. Guilt, worry and concern because haven't achieved much.

Can look like great high or under achievers.

Marked contrast between high and low energy states.

Self-preoccupation leads to detachment, so can appear aloof, conceited, arrogant.

Can have problem fitting into the world.

Can suppress their perceptions in order to be accepted.

Those around them feel uncertain and insecure and don't understand them.

POWERFUL PEOPLE

For those who have been born into this world with power gained from past lives and the problem of fear left over from the reptilian age.

Can be heads of empires large or small.

Can rule by fear instead of love because of their own fear.

For those who change the world at a social and political level - they train, change others. Leaders and achievers. They teach in a practical way, can give others great experiences.

Have immense capacity.

Fear of their own power and need to prove themselves and have status may hold them back.

Need lots of support because they will move us all forward.

May seem paranoid, but they are so intelligent, perceptive and intuitive it is as if their obsessions are large ones.

NERVOUS SYSTEM

Powerful effect on cerebro-spinal axis. Great support to other remedies working on this - Phosphorus, Belladonna, Apis, Calc Carb.

Works on every nerve plexus in the body related to chakra energy.

Powerful effect on the central nervous system.

Nervous affections of those who are struggling a bit with the higher vibrations who need some adjustment.

Milky Way

Epilepsy: to complete the connection of those souls who leave their bodies too abruptly.

Brings nourishment to the nervous system, working spiritually to help us receive more power, more light, more love.

Tingling and horripilation coming and going in different places.

Convulsions and twitchings.

EMOTIONAL

Impatience.

Sense of loss. For those who've lost their heart, lost their inspiration. Feel alone.

Hard to receive love because they are paralysed with fear, yet demand love.

Problems in emotional relationships. Need to be in control. Crave love but it is difficult to allow it to flow through them.

Set great store by dignity - they are afraid to be foolish, to let joy into their lives.

Armour of anger.

Tend to be cultured - the avenue for joy for them - need to relax and have fun.

Very difficult sexuality - can attract violence around them, rarely to them because of the power they hold.

Capable of cruelty. Can be passionate. Practical.

GENERAL

Coldness: marked symptom of the remedy. Stone cold. Tears from coldness.

Affects the R side.

All excretory processes aided by remedy. Process of purification

Degenerative illnesses caused by fear.

Fidgety. Restless. Tired. Scattered.

Scattered minds - those who seek but can't get it together.

Travellers.

PHYSICAL

Head: pain head from vertex down L side of face and side of head with tingling > Lachesis.

Stiff neck at the back and hard to hold the head up. Neck pain.

Works on central cleft of pituitary.

Eyes: profound impact on sight and vision.

Helps sight physically and spiritually, clears the vision.

Eyes burning, watering, stinging.

Blindness.

Stomach: nausea.

Abdomen: sensation of bowels draining.

Female: sacral activity.

Problems with reproductive system.

Menses dragging with slight dribbling.

Sensation as of labour pains in cervix.

Labour-like pains extending down back and thighs.

For the time in pregnancy between conception and quickening.

Back: low back pain.

Extremities: icy feet.

L leg jumping and twitching

R arm in spasm, couldn't move it. L arm felt paralysed.

L shoulder pain. L arm and hand numb and tingling.

Heart: sensation as of a stone rising from the bottom of the heart.

Blood dyscrasias.

CONNECTIONS

Triangles and trilogies.

With radiation. It matches and goes beyond the radiation vibration. It will help the effects of radiation, to antidote it and will follow Plutonium and other radiation remedies.

Connects with DNA and activates or regains aspects of DNA which we have had before but lost.

Restores ancient powers that our ancestors had long time ago. Cleanses ancestral forces.

Violet light and Amethyst.

Milky Way

MIASMS

The original miasm. The remedy where all the miasms have apparently been treated and still the patient is unwell.

REMEDIES

Aurum and despair.

Sol. Diamond. Lachesis. Nux Vom. Anacardium. Lycopodium.

Works well with Arsenicum - has the restlessness and acute mind but higher motives and is not driven by fear.

Harnesses and increases the power of remedies to do with the heart, such as Oak, Natrum Mur, Arnica and Aconite.

Powerful link with Stonehenge (the remedy) through the Heart.

Connected to the note 'A'.

It is a third of the trilogy of Milky Way (Solar Fish), Goldfish and Silverfish that creates the whole, that encompasses the Trinity, that represents the Holy Spirit in its truest form yet manifested on earth.

Each accesses a different aspect of the soul. They are all universal. The moment between unity and plurality. Connected to geometry and number.

Silverfish represents the past, Goldfish the present, Milky Way and Silverfish the future.

It must only be given carefully and given when the patient has been prepared through Silverfish and Goldfish.

PRESCRIBING NOTES

Only to be used on those using the Heart Chakra the right way. Will not work for those not coming from the Heart.

Must be used by the Prescriber working from the Heart or will not work.

Need to be grounded to use it.

Good to give this remedy in combination with many others to enhance, expand the action of the remedies that are already in existence.

Two pictures of the remedy - the spiritual essence and its physical proving. Do not confuse them.

Can look like Aurum - ambition, the desire to reach the top, to be one of the best, but of a higher vibration. It will help Aurum to work well if given before - use a 200.

Use Chalice Well in 6x potency as drainage when using Milky Way.

For hopeless cases, beyond the resources of homeopathy, it brings light.

Its action is for 7 days, whether in essence or potentised, so it bears repetition in whatever potency.

Natrum Fluoraticum
Sodium Fluoride

S odium fluoride is a colourless or white crystalline powder or crystals with which we are all very familiar through its introduction into drinking water and toothpaste to supposedly prevent tooth decay (although it can actually lead to weaker teeth through fluorosis). It is also commonly used as an insecticide and as a treatment for some conditions in farm animals. It used to be used as rat poison. It is known to be highly toxic by ingestion, inhalation and skin contact. Fluorine is the most reactive, electronegative element and it is never found alone in nature but always in a compound with another element or elements. The fluoride added to our tap water is a product called silicofluoride which is a cheap, low grade compound produced as a toxic waste from phosphate fertilizer pollution scrubbers. Known as hexafluorsilicic acid, this compound also contains other toxic substances such as arsenic, beryllium, mercury, lead and many more. It also contains radioactive elements from the decay of radon found in the rocks from which the fertiliser is made. Intake of fluoride is further increased through the consumption of processed foods, particularly dried ones which are then reconstituted with fluoridated tap water, through processed drinks including wine and beer, pre-boned chicken, anaesthetics, cigarettes, fish, pesticides, teflon coated pans and air pollution.

Fluoride is considered a trace element because only small amounts are present in the body (about 2.6 grams in adults), and because the daily requirement for maintaining dental health is only a few milligrams a day. About 95% of the total body fluoride is found in bones and teeth. Fluoride taken in quantity over time slowly poisons the human body. Prolonged intake of treated water can lead to discolored, mottled or brownish enamel on the teeth and eventually disorders of the kidneys, liver and adrenal failure, heart and reproductive system and central nervous system problems. Hip fractures, bone cancer, thyroid cancer, irritable bowel syndrome, allergies, skeletal fluorosis, osteoporosis, decreased fertility and neurotoxic effects in the brain have also been attributed to fluoride toxicity. Young children and the elderly are particularly vulnerable. The long term effects of drinking treated water have never been properly monitored as laboratory tests with fluoride use a pure form of sodium fluoride rather than that which is actually put into the water

In spite of several fatalities, the lethal dose of sodium fluoride in man is not accurately known. A single dose of 5g of sodium fluoride may be considered lethal in an adult and as little as 0.5g in a child. However, dangerous poisoning has been reported after much lower doses. It is readily absorbed from the alimentary tract where it kills mucosal cells, leading to severe inflammation and bleeding. If death is not prompt, shock may arise not only from gastrointestinal damage but also from central vasomotor depression and from cardiac disturbances. The central nervous system is also poisoned. The initial symptoms of ingestion are a salty or soapy taste, salivation, nausea, burning or crampy abdominal pain, vomiting, diarrhoea (which may be bloody), dehydration and thirst. This is followed by muscle weakness, tremors, sometimes epileptiform convulsions, followed by central nervous depression. The last stage involves shock characterised by pallor, a weak and thready pulse (sometimes irregular), shallow unlaboured respiration, weak heart tones, wet cold skin, cyanosis and dilated pupils, followed almost invariably by death in 2 to 4 hours, usually due to respiratory arrest or to cardiovascular collapse. Kidney damage may arise as a direct toxic action or as a consequence of shock. There may also be metabolic and electrolyte disturbances, including hypocalcaemia, the effects of which include tremors, tetany, convulsions, cardiac arrhythmias, shock, respiratory arrest, and cardiac failure. Application on the skin produces superficial or deep burns and necrotic ulcers which are painful and heal slowly. Inhalation produces ulceration of the mucous membranes of the digestive and/or respiratory tracts.

ESOTERIC

A vast and enormous remedy. Its action is profound, peaceful and gentle. A remedy of illusions and delusions, full of paradoxes.

Takes you through the veil into the living reality of the spiritual worlds, especially into the ability to manipulate power and energy.

Linked to ancient ceremonies and rituals and their energy connection with God.

Linked to Lords of Karma and to the power of the sun.

Expands the inner vision.

Raises consciousness and brings awareness that evil is not negative and is there to bring us through into the light. Without the darkness we do not learn or move forwards.

Connected with disasters and physical changes on the planet. Will help people to understand why they are necessary.

Removes inhibitions and allows access to spiritual power and understanding.

Linked to initiations of self-knowledge and stimulates us to know ourselves truly.

Brings lightness and ethereality.

Helps the weary initiate to carry on.

For the arrogance of our age. For those in positions of power, heads of state, those thrusting forward with destructive policies.

Helps understanding. Brings humility and peace.

Brings you into your own power and removes the darkness.

Can release deep karmic blocks and lift the weight from an individual's shoulders.

Strong contact to alien energies.

Gives the ability to be in the present.

CHAKRAS

Links the Brow and Heart. Opens the Brow with the compassion of the Heart.

Opens the Heart to Christ consciousness.

Crown Chakra. Thymus Chakra. Upper Heart Chakra. Expands a focus at the Brow which is too narrow.

Releases a lot in the Heart and Solar Plexus. Combines the power of the Heart and Solar Plexus and works on the tensions between these two chakras.

Connects Brow and Crown Chakras. Connects Heart and Crown. Links Throat, Brow and Crown.

Connection with a seed of light which is a sense of purpose at the Brow Chakra connected energetically to the pituitary.

Reconnects the top and the bottom, the Base and the Crown.

Balances energy between Sacral, Base and Throat after a hysterectomy.

Clears blocks hidden within the psyche at the Heart, Thymus and Parathyroid Centres blocking the gateway to the higher chakras and heaven. Its energy releases the higher Centres.

Stimulates the higher Chakras to evolve and develop our healing awareness and ability. Clears stasis in the higher Centres from the parathyroid to the Crown, reawakens and enlivens the head chakras.

RADIATION & TECHNOLOGY

Huge affinity with radiation. Radiation damage and toxicity: one of the most powerful remedies. For those who work in the nuclear industry and the karma of those connected with nuclear power/weapons in the past.

Powerful remedy for radiation damage to the Throat Chakra and thyroid. Like Sea Salt protects them against radiation.

Connected to nuclear power and genetic engineering and will help people to see the right way to use this technology and to handle the negative forces connected with them.

TRANSFORMATION

Brings transformation and has the power to bring transition from one spiritual level to another and to speed up this process.

Helps us to take the next step in transformation. Helps to unlock movement forward.

Transitions from one extreme to another.

A breakthrough remedy, as in the change from season to season. The transmutation of the material to the immaterial. The change from darkness to light.

Linked to the gallbladder's power to break through obstruction and to initiate a new phase.

BRAIN & MENTAL FUNCTION

Paralysis of brain, mind and spirit. Like a zombie: no presence of mind, or spirit. Paralysis of the brain and nervous system causing negative states of mind.

Emotionless states.

Perception is altered on all levels of consciousness.

Blankness. An inability to think or intuit. Mental stasis. Congestion in the head and memory. Completely blocked; no spiritual contact, no intuition.

Completely cut off from intuition.

Floatiness. Difficulty concentrating. Dazed and stunned. Congested.

Things float into the mind and then float out again.

May talk in monosyllables or appear completely absent.

Those locked within themselves, troubled and confused. Confusion, chaos and losing things. Jumbled.

Allows the mind to smile, memory return and the brain to breathe again. Generates positive energy in the auric field.

CONSOLIDATION

Focuses scattered energy.

Disconnection caused by radiation.

The reverse of a nuclear explosion - brings back together energies which have been dispersed and scattered. Consolidates.

Brings you back to your Base Centre. Brings threads together and creates coherence.

Those who do not know if they are here or there. In and out of the body. Brings people back into their bodies.

NEW HEALING

Linked to new diseases which confuse the medical profession. Use this remedy in illnesses which have not been seen before. They may seem minor illnesses but do not respond to indicated treatment as they should.

Tunes us in to new ways of healing.

Awakens the memory of ancient healing techniques we have known in the past.

DYING

Profound link with the process of dying. For souls passing in shock and trauma, suddenly. For souls lost after trauma, the remedy can retrieve them and send them healing.

Could be put on a corpse round the fingernails in drops to aid the soul in separating gracefully from its body and moving on.

For those who have died as a result of radiation in any form.

BABIES & CHILDREN

Babies: emaciation or underweight at birth, premature, deformed, possibly from the radiation miasm.

Children: helps them to acknowledge the light they carry.

With Ash helps them through their schooling.

Hyperactivity. Autistic and vaccine damaged children.

EMOTIONAL

A superficial and illusory state of peace but underneath there is great fear, stress and trauma.

Darkness. As if encased in a thick black tar which wipes out any positive thoughts or emotions. No light, joy or beauty, want to give up but have to keep going.

For everything that has been buried within everyone's hearts.

Empowers and strengthens feelings of love. Brings joy, lightness and the potential for freedom of expression.

For people who are very black but you can see a little glimmer of light, of hope.

Profound effect on all negative states of mind with deep morbid and even suicidal depression.

All-engulfing black preventing people seeing what is going on, creating fear. People who are filled with fear, who are stuck, heavy and immobile.

For the fear in people from natural disasters, planetary changes, profound changes in their lives. Terror, panic, loss, falling from grace.

Panic, fear and despair that goes with lack of sense of purpose.

Great trauma connected to the throat.

Anxiety of conscience. Mental torture. Calms despair and brings hope.

For those who use violence in an attempt to resolve conflict - the remedy takes their understanding to a higher level.

Huge struggle inside the Thymus: desire to do the right thing but huge blockage preventing it. Know what they have to do but there is not the courage or belief in themselves to do it.

All kinds of perversions of desire.

GENERAL

Heaviness of the body as if lacking vitality. Limbs heavy.

Great heat. Hot flushing and dry heat especially on the sides of the head and face, of the ears, long lasting, one sided.

Works more on the left side of body.

Male dominated energy.

Cleansing.

Restlessness.

Strong desire for chocolate.

Natrum Fluoraticum

Cramps and spasms of every description in every organ - use in low potency. Eventually tetany and death. One of the best remedies for tetanus. For all states of tetany and the parathyroids.

Pain in a bone previously fractured - use with Symphytum.

For deformities.

Road accident victims.

Allergies. ME. MS. Precancerous states. Down's Syndrome. Parkinson's. Post viral states.

PHYSICAL

Head: migraine. Pain at occiput extending to temples. Electric shocks and head injuries.

Disorders of the brain and pituitary. Brain tumours especially those caused by radiation.

Ears: burning.

Face: pain in the R jaw and R face.

Throat: profound effect on the throat. Dryness. Pressing pain in the throat. As if been strangled.

Heart: pains and palpitations.

Urinary: for kidney energy and fluid retention.

Female: hysterectomy where the ovaries are left. Uterine problems such as fibroids before the menopause. Heavy menses with bright blood and no clots.

Spine: strong affinity. Helps to bring light down through the spine. Frees and opens it.

Nerves: dampened and eventually destroyed.

Blood: disordered cells.

CONNECTIONS

Linked to ancient civilisations especially Egypt at it its highest and most advanced spiritual point. Link with Egyptian cats.

Linked to level of masters of ancient civilsations where energy manipulated for good or evil.

Linked to the long ancestral line of human evolution.

For animals captured in zoos.

MIASMS

Works on every miasm but its base is syphilis.

Grossly syphilitic so its power is hidden. Deep syphilitic karma.

Carcinogenic state.

Radiation miasm.

REMEDIES

Works well with Ayahuasca and can show people the light, like magic.

Works well with Lotus and combined with Medorrhinum, Syphilinum or Carcinosin.

Psorinum: where the carcinogenic state meets the psoric.

Similar to and linked with Plutonium in the sense that we are half animal and half divine.

Sphere of action overlaps Himalayan Blue Poppy and the two can be used together.

Amethyst. Arsenicum. Berlin Wall. Calc Carb. Carbo Veg. Cotton. Holly Berry. Ivy. Opium. Phosphorus. Rose Quartz. Sea Holly. Sulphur. Winchelsea Water. Almond.

PRESCRIBING NOTES

Remedy in gross form has poisoned humanity for aeons. It is used by many forces of darkness within governing bodies to poison and pollute mankind. All patients could benefit from a dose of this remedy as all souls are poisoned by it. A desperately needed remedy.

The effect of the remedy spreads out from the prescriber and those taking it to affect all those around. A remedy with a powerful auric field. Can cut through all other vibrations.

The patient may draw you into their state of delusion so it may be a difficult remedy to perceive for them.

Remedy does not need to be repeated often - carries on working deeply and slowly.

A remedy that needs to be put into the water supply.

Nettle Urtica urens

T his is the well known remedy made from the small stinging nettle, used homeopathically mainly for its physical connections with the skin, joints and the kidneys. The nettle loves soil which has been disturbed and which is rich in the phosphates and nitrogen found in manure, consequently it grows wherever there has been human habitation. Even sites of medieval settlements can still be marked by beds of nettles. Nettles have long been used as a food and a medicine and for making cloth and string.

The Nettle flowers from June to September usually reaching a height of 2 to 3 feet. Its perennial roots are creeping, so it multiplies quickly. The whole plant is downy and also covered with stinging hairs. The genus name Urtica comes from the Latin verb urere, meaning 'to burn,' because of the stinging hairs along the stem. It is an odd (but not to homeopaths) fact that the juice of the nettle will antidote the stings from the hairs, as will Dock, Rosemary, Mint and Sage.

The name Nettle is said to derive from the Anglo-Saxon for needle, either because of the stings or more likely because the plant was used for making thread before the general use of flax. Its fibre is very similar to that of hemp or flax and it was used for the same purposes, from making cloth of the finest texture down to the coarsest, such as sailcloth, sacking, cordage, etc. In Hans Andersen's fairy-tale of the Princess and the Eleven Swans, the coats she wove for them were made of Nettles. In the sixteenth and seventeenth century Nettle fibres were still used in Scotland for weaving the coarser household napery. However the fibre is more difficult to extract than from flax and is produced in less quantities. As nettles like to grow in rich fertilised soil, it is also an uneconomic crop to grow for fibre.

Traditionally nettles have been used as a diuretic, to build and cleanse the blood and for arthritis and rheumatism, their anti-inflammatory effects having been confirmed by clinical research. Externally it has been used to improve the appearance of the hair and is said to be a remedy against oily hair and dandruff. Its traditional use for allergies and rhinitis has also been confirmed by clinical trials. In Germany nettle is sold as a herbal drug for prostate diseases and recent research has found it useful in prostatitis and benign prostate hyperplasia. Its diuretic effect may make the nettle useful in high blood pressure. It is also used herbally as a blood cleanser.

As a food nettles were valuable as fodder for livestock, being rich in nutrients and losing their sting once they had wilted. Nettles have also been a food for people for thousands of years, being freely available and rich in minerals and vitamin C.

The nettle is also a vital part of the ecology. In Britain upwards of thirty insects feed solely on the Nettle plant, but flies have a distaste for it, and a fresh bunch of Nettles will keep a larder free from them. Nettles also produce a permanent green dye.

ESOTERIC

Strong connection with light. Helps in bringing light down

Promotes the expression of light and our contact with our inner light; our own light. Helps us to know we are beings of light on a physical level - not just a spiritual level, that we are perfect as we are; we shine with our own light and for this we bear a great responsibility - passing on our light to others, and holding the light strong around the earth.

Hunger not for food, but for spiritual sustenance.

For people who are not completely good, who are tainted easily with darker energy.

This remedy beings you home, gives security, comfort, the knowledge that you are perfect as you are in God's sight. No need to struggle, no need to fight. Relax and Be.

An enormous amount to this remedy on every level.

A good remedy for dying, like going home, back to the angels, one's family. A very happy feeling, death is nothing to fear.

Goes forwards and backwards in time. Heals the ancestors.

Strong connection with nature, with the earth and things that grow in the earth.

An outdoor remedy. Lovely quiet gardens. About the sun feeding the earth. Everything we need is in nature.

Like being in the garden but without the strains and stresses, no pressure to do any work, nothing needs doing, just all the joy of life.

CHAKRAS

Profound effect on the Brow Chakra and pituitary gland.

Stuckness around the Third Eye.

Great stillness with Brow Chakra; gives detachment but with compassion.

Removes shock lodged in Brow. For those in a state of gentle absence through shock, who no longer connect with people; they drift in life.

Profound effect on releasing Sacral Chakra.

Great warmth at the Solar Plexus.

Removes tension at the Solar Plexus.

Nettle

RELAXING

Profound gentleness and softness.

Lovely calmness.

Feeling of being comfortable in my body. Serene in my body.

Need to be very still and quiet.

Feeling of being in a very wide space, very quiet and very open and still.

A feeling of contentment.

Brings stillness, gentleness, for stress, those who are too busy, have too many things to do. Slows down the pace of life so we can cope. Within its gentle loving energy we can feel good about ourselves, release self-criticism.

Takes you out of time and gives a different perspective.

Brings deep relaxation, promotes sleep.

TRAUMA

Good for those damaged as children from lack of love and affection. The thymus in us all; goes into the karmic blueprints, therefore into DNA.

Humble little remedy of much power - a remedy to heal the traumas to come.

For traumatised children, to bring them peace, relaxation, calmness.

Enables you to release deep hurt. Tensions that have held you up all your life can go with this remedy.

Has enormous healing power and potential for good, like Arnica for the soul. Remedy to be used frequently, constantly.

Remedy to keep calm and centred.

A remedy for the aftermath of mass destruction in cities. For the numbness that follows and to clear the toxicity. For the children who survive to help them into the New Age.

It will help us get through the destruction before the good comes - on a personal level as well as on a bigger scale.

CLEANSING

A connection with the sea - for cleansing, re-birth, rejuvenation.

Removes toxicity from the earth. A great cleanser.

Can be sprayed on the earth for the effect humanity has had on the earth, on and in buildings.

The earth cries out for this remedy - especially cities. Anywhere man has trodden, this remedy is needed

EMOTIONAL

Sadness.

Lost identity and sense of purpose.

A very strong feeling of disconnection and separation was felt by many provers.

Releases self-criticism, self-mortification, self-judgement.

For workaholics, those who are driven, enables them to feel good about themselves. to no longer have to prove themselves. Helps people to feel loved.

For victims, those trodden on, those who can't stand up for themselves, those with a weak ego.

GENERAL

A remedy for autumn and winter.

Vaccination damage

For anorexics and bulimics and for those who hate their bodies.

Important remedy for children.

Remedy has a male energy.

Itching and tingling in the night.

Pulsing though body.

Water balance in the body - use with Apis.

Effects of external toxins: e.g. skin eruptions, ulceration of the eyes.

PHYSICAL

Head: affects both lobes of the pituitary.

  Numbness around the face.

  Tingling round the head, face, lips.

  Slight vertigo, wants to move.

Mouth: gritty splinters in the mouth and throat - sharp.

  Throat feels numb from the neck downwards.

  Strong sensation in the mouth, needing to open it, to speak out.

Neck & throat: tension at throat - grief held in. A throat remedy.

Tension and stiffness across top of back, neck and shoulders. Aching throat.

Lungs: many symptoms, cancers, thick black, choking matter in the lungs, killing people.

Stomach: hot, burning sensation.

Solar plexus - feels empty, flushes of heat at solar plexus.

Kidneys: important remedy.

Female: sensation as if vulva swollen, engorged with desire for sex.

For frigidity, promotes enjoyment of sex.

Nervous system: motor neurone disease. MS.

Nerves affected generally, especially the nerves of the teeth.

Tingling sensations with numbness.

Extremities: tingling in the feet.

CONNECTIONS
Numbers 8, 1 and 81.

The colour orange.

Golden butterfly.

Moorland, heather, sunshine, bees.

Celandine and other yellow star shaped flowers

REMEDIES
Calc Carb. Sea Salt, Diamond Essence, radiation remedies, Plutonium, Buddleia.

Base Chakra remedies. Tree remedies

PRESCRIBING NOTES
A remedy that will be especially needed in the future.

Olive (Rhodes) Olea europaea

The olive is an evergreen tree growing to 50 ft. in height with a spread of about 30 ft. with graceful, billowing branches and gnarled trunk. Olive trees can live for 500 years. and are tenacious, easily sprouting back even when chopped to the ground. A long, hot growing season is required to properly ripen the fruit and the tree can survive the necessary extended hot, dry periods because of its small, leathery leaves. The small, fragrant, cream-coloured olive flowers are largely hidden by the grey-green leaves and are of two kinds: a perfect flower containing both male and female parts and another with stamens only. The flowers are largely wind pollinated with most olive varieties being self-pollinating. The olive never bears fruit in the same place twice.

Raw olives contain an alkaloid that makes them bitter and unpalatable and they have to be cured to be eaten. Traditionally the near-ripe olives are soaked in a series of lye solutions, then in water and finally a mild saline solution.

The olive is native to the Mediterranean region, tropical and central Asia and various parts of Africa. The olive has a history almost as long as that of Western civilization, its development being one of civilized man's first accomplishments. Olive seed which is 8,000 years old has been found in Spain and olives were being grown in Crete at least 5,500 years ago. All the ancient peoples around the rim of the Mediterranean have laid claim to the discovery of the olive tree.

The olive branch has long been regarded as a symbol of peace and goodwill and the olive tree a symbol of immortality. It has also always been linked to fertility, strength, wealth, victory, glory, purification and sanctity. 6,000 years ago the ancient Egyptians believed that it was Isis, the greatest of all the goddesses and wife of Osiris, who had taught mankind how to grow and use olives. In Greek mythology it was Athena, goddess of wisdom and peace, who gave humanity the gift of the olive tree. Hebrew legend has it that a cedar, a cypress and an olive tree grew on Adam's grave on the slopes of mount Tabor and the Old and New Testaments abound in references to the olive. An olive tree branch was the award to the winners of the first Olympic Games.

The benefits of olive oil as a food are now well known. Olive oil offers protection against heart disease by controlling cholesterol levels. It has a beneficial effect on ulcers and gastritis, activates the secretion of bile and pancreatic hormones and so diminishes gallstone formation. It is highly digestible, has a mild laxative effect, creates an appetite, helps with the *absorption of fat-soluble vitamins and decreases the risk of developing breast and colon cancer. The oil may also help non-insulin dependent diabetes and slow down the ageing process and the deterioration of cells. Olive oil has been used since Biblical times to keep skin soft and supple and to treat eczema, dandruff and psoriasis. It has also been used for consecrating and anointing and in lamps.*

The leaves have been used to treat nearly every ailment from arthritis to warts. The olive leaf has significant antimicrobial and antiseptic properties and is now used to inhibit the progress of many viruses including HIV and to treat a long list of other afflictions. Olive leaf is used as a Bach flower remedy to treat those who are physically or emotionally exhausted.

The olive for this remedy was green and came from Rhodes.

ESOTERIC

A simple but precious and sacred remedy. The more simple a remedy the deeper its effect.

Brings peace and stillness.

Restores individual into consciousness of contact with God, to aspiration without desire and being in but not of the world.

Allows you to see truth behind facade of materialism and wisdom in small things.

Links us with the nature spirits of sea and sand.

Reminds you who you are, keeps you contained and sure of your own process.

Great auric protector.

For those who are psychic sponges - will calm this process and decrease their sensitivity so they can live in the world.

For possessions and all obsessive states.

CLEANSING & RELEASE OF THE PAST

Great purifying effect. Great cleansing power. Can go into the past very deeply, even into past incarnations.

Helps to lift the lid off things that are deeply hidden.

Brings light to hidden things, like opening an old wound festering, unknown and invisible, so can release deep pain.

For people who won't listen, won't hear truths because of their fear of change.

t can touch on the residue that is left around our earth plane from incarnations that are pre-human.

Releases hurts and deep shocks on every level of consciousness, even hurts from past lives. Memories or dreams will flood into consciousness as this clearing takes place. As this happens will be freed from influence of those who have hurt you and release much negative karma. As this happens, you begin to breathe.

Touches on past incorrect use of magic where this has been used not entirely in the service of the light but for selfish reasons of power and ego.

Releases incorrect use of sexual energy with magic, removes guilt and allows power to be used with wisdom, love and humility.

Will heal those who have abused and improperly raised kundalini energy and will heal spinal distortions which have resulted from this.

Can remove spells and curses which run through family lines for generations.

Brings us into truth and responsibility. To face the reality of all we have done and to experience the consequences.

Brings opportunity to see our past mistakes, accept them and repair damage and have their weight transformed into love, joy and forgiveness, melting the heart.

Helps unpick knots of care, past worries and fears and consequences on physical and etheric body.

Breaks links and inappropriate connections.

After a bereavement and the patient feels that part of them went also, or a sense the soul has not moved on and is living through the patient.

EMOTIONAL

For those hooked into drugs obsessively as way of hiding from their pain.

For those who opt out of life, who have lost their way. Will help greatly given daily over a period of time. Will help them find their way back from the slippery slope.

Calms hurt minds and bodies. Great tranquiliser.

Soothes agitation and irritation on any level for any reason.

Obsessive thoughts going round and round.

Very deep sadness. Sad and tearful.

Strong sense of a struggle.

Olive

Increases self-esteem markedly, good for those who are shy and do not show faces.

Can bring in the sun, the light when there has been great darkness.

Works well on those fearful of public speaking for it brings them into their own power.

GENERAL

Excellent remedy for all parents, especially new parents to bring understanding and insight into their role to allow them to contact the new being and to understand its needs. Should help to stop parents vaccinating their children. Give to both new parents.

Powerful when there is a cross link between two incarnations such as when there have been twins in the womb and one has not survived.

Linked to the breath.

Good for those out of the rhythm of life, for those who are trying to escape their incarnation.

All carcinogenic states - in mind before manifests on physical level or on physical level for immune system.

Itching and twitching.

Strengthens bones, hair and nails.

Slows a metabolism which is too fast.

Calms adrenalin so can be at peace and see way forward.

Very cold.

Great heat all over.

PHYSICAL

Head: great used on the brain. Brain tumours.

Eyes: improves quality of vision.

Stomach: calms acidity in digestive tract at very physical level.

Can heal ulcers in any part of digestive tract.

Abdomen: helps with inflammation of pancreas and spleen.

Skin: will help all skin conditions, it is great balm internally and externally. Good as cream.

Spine: afflictions of.

Extremities: affinity with soles of feet.

Pains in left shoulder, knotted.

Affects all joints: rigidity and degeneration.

PRESCRIBING NOTES

When the patient first takes the remedy, they may experience a physical, mental or spiritual aggravation. This may last for several days as the purification effect works its way through, then calmness will follow. If the remedy works this way, it has reached a deep level of the psyche quickly and is a good sign.

If agitation occurs after several days or weeks, the patient may need a dose of Carcinosin.

It can put people through a difficult time, with things that don't want to be seen, felt or heard.

Orange

A s the colour has been named after the fruit, one wonders what the name for the colour was before oranges arrived in western Europe, or even if the colour was in our consciousness before this. Orange, a combination of red and yellow, is the least popular of colours. It is stimulating and energising, encouraging joy, enthusiasm and self confidence. It enhances sociability, creativity and independence. Its negative aspects include difficulty in interacting with others and unsociability, pride and exhibitionism and dependency. It is connected with self-respect and boundaries, both our own and those of others. It is said to relate to the ultimate feelings of fulfillment as in sex and childbirth. In the current popular system of chakra and colour association, orange relates to the Sacral chakra. In the remedy, its energy is raised to the higher creative chakra connected to the mind and spiritual union - the Brow. In Tibet, orange is a popular colour used with bright blue, and has always been linked to death. An orange light and sandalwood incense are burned in the room where someone is dying. The Book of the Dead is read to them, to aid their transition into the Clear Light and to keep them from the attachments, thoughts and emotions which would draw them back into another incarnation.

ESOTERIC

It allows the expression of higher consciousness in the life, in the physical world. It precipitates the manifestation of spirituality throughout the being.

Refines the thinking process, clarifies the thoughts and turns them towards higher things and to matters celestial.

Links us to past wisdom through our consciousness of dream states.

Allows access to the heart of truth. It allows you to speak your truth, to be at one with your true nature.

Helps to concentrate and focus energies to one point.

Fine-tuning for those who already have a certain spiritual order in their lives but want to refine it and to work up to a higher level.

Brings strength and the ability to empower, especially spiritually.

Works best on initiates with certain amount of understanding but can also bring this understanding to those who are ready.

Children benefit greatly from the light of this remedy for they are not far from the truth. Helps them to keep their spiritual candle lit throughout their incarnation and maintain their contact with God.

Excellent remedy for all healers, true healers who heal in spirit of the truth and love for it will help them to be discerning and see.

Opens doors on any level. Gives enlightenment.

A space-maker. Deals with all kinds of congestion.

Brings purification, stillness and calm, quietness enabling you to see with all eyes.

Brings true intuition and ability to discern the truth. Enables you to separate what is true from what is false.

Divine grace is accessed through this remedy.

CHAKRAS

Brings strength and confidence and a sense of unity, a mind-body connection, via the Heart.

Opens the Brow Chakra.

It stimulates the Brow Centre and the Heart in the Mind, and opens the Heart and the Mind in the Heart.

It is intimately connected with the Brow Centre and the middle lobe of the pituitary.

The remedy enters through Brow Centre and then affects every Centre and part of the being producing a quietness within. This quietness enables healing to flow to wherever it is required. It enables the true eye to be opened with no judgement. The eye of God. It is indeed a remedy which all sensitives and healers will benefit from.

A remedy for the Thymus Centre and the Throat.

Opens up Throat and Sacral Chakras.

PEACE & STILLNESS

It can bring peace so we can sit stable, strong, silent, and so that all our thoughts, feelings and physical powers are concentrated, focussed and linked with the Divine.

The stillness helps to create a greater integration in the patient so the concentration and memory improve. It also helps to heal all the miasms which tend to have a rather diffusing process, for its energy moves all through every layer of the being and being cannot resist, for once that stillness enters, resistance begins to break down.

Enhances inner stillness.

It is the eye of the storm, the point of stillness.

Resolution. A point of clarity. Moment of birth and the moment of death. It is what we see at the birth and death of the day. It is not something we can grasp but it is within us. Its power is in its stillness and in its ability to switch off the mental faculties, for stillness of mind is gift from God. With stillness of mind, all is possible, many doors in deep layers of consciousness can be opened. Once this process has been initiated, perfect intuition results, for no clutter is present. Fear is removed, the mind stilled and light brought into the consciousness.

PROTECTION

A great protector, bringing with it much understanding of what is correct for individual on all levels.

It will help to afford protection from radiation, as many of new remedies do. This remedy does so on a deeper level. It can be given alone to stop radiation penetrating through deep levels which blocks cure all the time. Once radiation penetrates it makes the syphilitic miasm more difficult to understand and to see. This will protect the spirit from contagion more than the physical part of the body.

BIRTH, DEATH & TRANSITION

Good for the newborn and the dying.

A remedy to help grief for the life left behind when someone moves from being focussed in the material world to being more at one with the spirit.

Towards the end of life it stimulates the being to seek out that which remains unfinished, to clean up the messes outstanding, to release anger and resentment. It opens the heart to forgiveness and allows the soul to move forward into the next life with less baggage. It allows the completion of one state and the movement to the next, a higher state of consciousness.

It has the purifying quality of fire and will cleanse and help destroy the old to make way for the new.

It assists greatly in the birth process and in the death process - transitions. It can be used with great effect with Sandalwood to help the spirit to depart in the correct manner, enabling it to pass into the light and not get lost in realms of darkness on the way through.

A door-opener to other forms of experience new to us.

GETTING ON THE RIGHT PATH

t has enormous activity and energy, great stimulating power. It is an enabler.

t stimulates the being to complete those tasks which remain undone, on whatever level.

t creates an awareness of what one should be doing with the incarnation. It makes clear the life path and creates the changes necessary for putting the feet upon this path.

t enables the being to find their correct blueprint again and in doing so brings them back to life.

t balances positive and negative energies and therefore helps in all states of initiation and change into different states of consciousness.

GROUNDING

Brings practical down-to-earth spirituality.

It is a powerful earthing remedy. It brings much physical power and organisation on the earth plane.

Gives expansion, protection and groundedness to receive and create a pathway to truth.

Helpful for people stuck in strong egos, the head. Grounding.

GENERAL

Helps to solidify, concentrate and manifest our thought forms in our physical body, both positive and negative, thus grounding our truth and allowing the light of self-realisation to come through.

Tones the physical body, the skin, muscles, tendons, bones and the spine, organises the discs, increases the flow and straightens the channels of energy up and down through the nadi and the nerve centres.

Strengthens the aura. It can seal it from negative influences, plug the holes with a strong etheric cement.

For physically weakened states that need tone and structure, where the will has been weak or where nutritional considerations have not been met.

Has a powerful effect on many physical systems, once the spirit of truth has been centred.

Balm for hurt and destroyed minds.

Orange

PHYSICAL

Eyes: connected with eyes. Eyes aching and out of focus. For vision on all levels.

Lungs: breathing difficulties, asthma. Clears respiratory passages.

Kidneys: strong kidney remedy. Good for nephritis.

Calms down overactive adrenal glands.

Spleen: profound effect on spleen energy.

Circulation: assists the flow of blood correctly and brings the quality of blood to the point of truth for the individual.

Extremities: cramp in R foot and toes. Sharp pain R inguinal ligament.

CONNECTIONS

Closely linked with spirals and tied up with genetic material.

Mercury poison from amalgam fillings. where this has penetrated the spiritual being and created blocks. Blocks upon blocks occur and miasms hide as a result.

Chanting and spiritual voices singing, and greatly so with the seed mantra OM in which all is contained.

REMEDIES

Affinity with Goldfish and Silica, to bring strength with refinement.

Hazel. Amber. Diamond.

PRESCRIBING NOTES

If Orange is given before the indicated remedy that is not working well, it would help it to work. If given afterwards it will also help to push the patient's remedy along. It is also good for patients who mentally block taking remedies from fear.

Moldavite given before Orange may help, if you intuit the patient will benefit from the speeding up of karma as they move to this still point. It will guarantee an aggravation, but will work.

The remedy has an essence and a picture, but prescribe on your intuition and listen to what the patient's spirit is telling you rather than what their mind is telling you.

It is very important in its use that the Heart Centre of the prescriber is open. This humility is such a deep key.

Only for those who already have a well-developed Brow Chakra or it could be quite destructive. Do not give to someone whose life is in chaos.

This can be an uncomfortable remedy, for it will shine light on dark places and reveal what would be forgotten or hidden. It will bring about upheavals in life as a consequence.

Must be given with caution and those with big ego may receive a dose now and again to help them see their truth. It does its work at the back of the pituitary gland where the ability to lie changes the individual's spirit of truth. They lie to themselves and the ego becomes enhanced. The remedy works well in this area. It will cause an aggravation.

It works well on individuals who tell lies and then believe them to be the truth, but give with caution over a long period of time when you intuit or it may cause some madness, but only temporarily; homeopathy cannot do that kind of damage.

Phantom Quartz

A phantom quartz is a clear quartz crystal which appears to have a small whitish 'ghost' crystal inside it. It is said to symbolise universal awareness and to represent the many experiences and phases possible within one lifetime. It is one of the crystals which can be used for the redemption and healing of the earth: the phantom emanates the energy to save and renew the spiritual health of the earth. It helps the energy of the earth to return to its original state before the traumas inflicted on it by humanity. The crystal aids meditation and facilitates access to the higher realms of knowledge and to the records of one's past lives, but from the perspective of the higher self. It can also heal the mental and emotional states which may arise as a result of healing these past lives. The crystal can help you to meet your personal, spiritual guide and to communicate with him/her. On a physical level it is said to help with hearing disorders and to promote clairaudience.

ESOTERIC

Represents the potential of mankind and its development. Will become more generally useful as Age progresses. Remedy of transformation, regeneration, revelation.

Renews contact with God where the will has been destroyed. It restores faith in oneself and restores contact with God and all the higher forces that are around for all of us to tap into if we choose.

Helps to allow shocks and blocks from past karmic fear or emotional impact to be evolved. Does not need to be conscious awareness for this to happen. Allows old patterns held by these blockages to dissolve.

Gives access to another dimension which we can touch but not stay in; only those correctly on the path of light can experience this dimension truly. Evokes energies and spirits from beyond the veil.

Brings peace and serenity.

Remedy brings into consciousness all negative karma and usually that of a masculine and yang nature and this must be released. Doubts and fears are no longer essential. Once this negative karma is released it enables you to take responsibility for yourself and your own karma, to face your karma, to use your blueprint in a new and positive way.

It makes people see their negativity and if they are not prepared to look at themselves it can turn in on them, bring up the syphilitic miasm.

Linked to shamanic processes, soul retrieval, shape shifting. Can enhance astral travel.

CHAKRAS

Rebalances all the Chakras and enables you to use your astrological chart in positive way.

Promotes the flow of love through the Heart Centre up into the Brow Centre and awakens its higher powers. Focuses energy at the Brow Centre. Will help to open up the higher levels of Brow Centre whilst staying earthed.

Releases stuck Thymus energy.

Opens and clears the Throat.

Brings an opening of the Heart.

MALE/FEMALE ENERGY

Heals massive splits in consciousness.

Rebalances masculine-feminine energy and brings you to a point of equilibrium but only by facing your own negativity. Balances female and male sexuality, yin and yang, positive and negative, light and dark.

Transmutes base, crude, sexual energy into higher, more refined thoughts, energy, vibrations.

Men who don't want children and are promiscuous, or who can't have children because of damage from the Pill, drug abuse, etc. Throat Chakra connected.

NOT FULLY INCARNATED

For those who are here but not here. Out of body states.

For those who have incarnated wrongly, who do not fit into their lives.

Helps souls to become fully human: those who can't quite come into human evolution, those lost between levels, not grounded in this life.

For those who resign from the world because it is all too difficult, so they absent themselves: society's drop outs. Remedy helps people to cope with the world, be part of it.

Eccentricity, obscure thought processes, failure to connect with those around, peculiar to themselves. Helps them to live more in world, with others.

MATERIALISM & DELUSION

Promotes growth on all levels. For those who are reluctant to grow, whose growth has been inhibited. Gives people new choices, opportunities to get on the right path. Enables them to see differently, see another way.

For people on a materialistic path, who need to take on new patterns and put life on more spiritual and life-enhancing course.

Will help heal people who are so career orientated they lose touch with their creativity, especially career women.

Those with a strong connection with the spirit world who choose not to use it.

For someone rigid, unmoving, highly conventional, black and white, refusing for sense of security to step into grey areas and into spirituality.

People who are clever-brained. Those who would rather win the argument than see the Truth. Linked to illusion, Neptune. Those in state of illusion or delusion.

Enables you to see the truth in those around you, to discern truth from illusion. To see how mutated the truth is within some individuals.

Those with a credible belief system but who live in world of delusion.

Those who use spiritual information wrongly, for their own ends, for their ego.

People who force the pace of their development.

DRUGS

Useful in getting people off drugs, to produce in them some kind of awareness. Can help souls who are partially lost through drug experiences.

Use with caution for those using cannabis and ecstasy. Will not help them stop drugs and not safe while still taking them, but once stop will help repair damage.

For women on HRT which keeps them fixed in a materialistic mode.

EMOTIONAL

Fear. Fears and panics. Fear shackles the heart. Helps in tests of fear and panic, where fear would interfere with progress. Will take you to still point of cosmos where all souls who have ever linked with can join and help you. Not to be used flippantly.

Disorientation.

Doubt. Doubt and depression.

GENERAL

Long term chronic illness. Resigned with despair and hopelessness to their condition. Can restore hope and vision.

Strong effect on nervous system.

Lack of energy states and motivation; physical and mental weakness.

Those in state of exhaustion from service to others - therapists, esp. those heart centred.

For those affected by water: water balance in the body, weather, tides.

Very restless. Fidgeting. Lack of focusing; disorientation. Lack of concentration.

Hot, sweating, faint and dizzy. Sensation as if the body is cut in half down the middle.

Leukaemia. Schizophrenia. Manic depression.

PHYSICAL

Head: dull pain in R temple.

Heart: tremendous palpitations - cannot breathe fast enough to keep up with heart beats. Heart beating very erratically and very fast. Tightness and palpitation of the heart.

Lungs: not enough air.

Stomach: nausea

CONNECTIONS

Link between Phantom Quartz and the permanent seed atom.

Many of the ancients used this crystal on physical level in the centre of a magic wand, for its power is great.

Strong link with water and how water can be used to move negative feelings away leaving space for light and positive feelings. Linked to swamps, mists, neglected wastelands of water where discarnate energies can easily float.

Phantom Quartz holds the wisdom of Atlantis, with clear quartz as its partner.

REMEDIES

Azure blue. Unicorn. Rainbow will destroy its action.

PRESCRIBING NOTES

This remedy is best made three days before the full moon enters the sign of Aquarius, with clear crystal in between this crystal and the receptive medium.

Phantom Quartz

Can be used when a remedy is running too fast and the patient cannot cope. This will slow down its action and minimise aggravations so the patient can cope.

Use any potency - the remedy works much the same on all levels.

Use with Syphilinum and Arnica for those in a coma - it will help greatly.

Use with throat remedies like Lachesis, Causticum, Mercury and Lettuce.

The crystal will help to clear your channels. You can sleep with it under your pillow asking for the special help that it can give you before you go to sleep.

Call up help from beyond the veil when using this remedy for patient.

Rose (Pink)

This remedy was made from leaf, stem, thorn and flower of three pink roses: Ispahan, a Damask rose, said to have been brought back from the middle east by the Crusaders; The Queen of Denmark, an Alba rose that goes back to the Middle Ages and New Dawn, a climber bred in 1930. All are highly scented.

The Rosaceae family includes apple, pear, cherry, plum, strawberry and some ornamental plants but roses are the only member of the genus Rosa. Wild roses stretch in the northern hemisphere from the Arctic Circle to Abyssinia but none is indigenous to the southern hemisphere. There are several hundreds of wild varieties, most have single flowers and large decorative fruits. There are thought to be 14 native species in Britain, one of which, the white rose rosa avensis, is thought to be the rose for which the Romans called England Albion, or the white one. The rose is the flower of England, as Oak is the tree, but neither the red of Lancaster nor the white of York, finally united by Henry Tudor in1485, is an English native, the red being a French gallica, and the white being a cross between the native avensis and the damscena rose.

There are now many different types of roses: Gallicas, centifolias, albas, mosses, portlands, robust bourbons, noisettes, climbers, ramblers, rugosas, polyanthas and floribundas. The shape and texture of the rose is incredibly varied, from the scrambling wild varieties, to the blowsy blooms of the deep-cupped hybrid musks. The roots of roses reach a long way down, which is why they hate being disturbed. This also makes them very vigorous and able to withstand drought and harsh weather, although they are now susceptible to pollution. Gurudas (in Gem Essence and Vibrational Healing) says that roses are gradually being removed from the earth plane. They fared better when there was coal smoke in the air as this killed off many of the fungi and pests that plague them.

Roses have been cultivated for thousands of years and have been used more than any other flower. They are depicted in ancient Egyptian and Cretan frescoes and were grown in gardens in Persia at least 600 years BC. The Romans grew fields of roses for their petals which were strewn over returning heroes and over couches and funeral biers. Many of the roses now in Europe were brought back from the crusades. The first was the strongly scented Gallica rose, called the apothecary's rose, which formed the basis of the perfume industry and was the rose used for medical purposes throughout Europe. Pliny lists over thirty ailments which could be cured by the rose and by the 18th century over a third of all herbal preparations included some

Rose

part of it. Rose oil and rose water have been valued as a perfume for thousands of years and the oil is still a major ingredient in the most expensive of modern perfumes, having a scent which lasts for weeks.

The first great garden collection of roses was made by the Empress Josephine at Malmaison when she was married to Napoleon. She had at least 250 varieties, which she employed Redouté to paint and catalogue, starting a French passion for roses. It was the French who were responsible for most of the cross-breeding and methodical labelling of roses in the 19th century, producing the Bourbons and the Blush Noisettes from crossing European and Chinese roses.

Roses have been important symbolically for as long as they have been cultivated. The rose was central to Persian mystical poetry and in the east roses were used like lotuses to symbolise the chakras. This has persisted into the western mystical tradition: the Rosicruscians base their name on them (the Rosy Cross) and a rose is part of the symbol for the White Eagle Lodge. In language, we use the rose as a symbol of easy, pleasant times: we talk of days of wine and roses, life being a bed of roses, looking back through rose tinted spectacles. In poetry it is an often used symbol and image for love and the heart. Today the rose, especially the red, is as much as ever a symbol of love.

It would seem that the rose has always been associated above all with love and death. For the Greeks and Romans the red rose was the emblem of Venus and love and was also used in funeral rites. From mediaeval times, the rose was related to love and grief and the passing of time. Monastic burial grounds were planted as rose gardens, and roses of great age can be found in old cemeteries throughout Europe. Gardens of remembrance are still planted as rose gardens. The rose symbolises eternal life and the transcendence of death by love.

The rose has been heavily associated with Christianity over the centuries. The early church adopted it, along with so much else, from the pagans. In Druidic ceremonies, a red rose symbolised the air element, associated with the heart chakra. The red rose became a symbol of the blood of the martyr and also the 'Flower of God' - the five petals representing Christ's bleeding wounds and its thorns his crown. In the middle ages it became particularly associated with the Virgin Mary, especially the white rose which was seen as symbolising purity. The rosary, a string of beads common to many religions used as an aid in counting prayers, derives its name from the practice of making these beads from rose petals formed into pellets and strung together.

There are countless myths and stories associated with the rose throughout Europe and the East, tales of enchantment, magic and witchcraft, most involving affairs of the heart, for it is always associated with love.

ESOTERIC

Remedy will do whatever we want it to do. An infinite picture. There is no fixed picture. For all who work in the light. Changeable in its qualities and adapts more than any other to energy of person who receives it. It will do whatever is right for that person at that time.

It is awe-inspiring in its breadth. Beautiful.

Ethereal, nebulous, delicate, lighthearted and elusive in its energy.

For all those on the spiritual path but especially children yet to come. Truly a remedy for the New Age. It gives a direct link with God. Facilitates channelling, meditating.

Brings much more light and lightens the spirit. Bringing light from darkness.

Helps heal the planet when dark forces get in.

Focuses energy in one small point; connected with materialisation and transformation of energy.

Remedy is very powerful and will bring up a lot of dark and painful karma for people: ancestral, about separation, from abusing spiritual wisdom.

Brings out secrets, dark things, hidden truths and pain.

Helps bring people closer to nature.

CHAKRAS

Aligns all centres and allows energy to move unimpeded up and down the spine.

Particular affinity with Base, Heart, Throat and Brow.

For those caught in materialism at the Base.

Brings the heart and mind together and brings peace, love, wisdom and power.

Releases deep grief held in the Heart through the Thymus, Brow and Throat.

Stuckness at the Solar Plexus. Helps raise energy from the Solar Plexus into the Heart and beyond.

Relates to the central pillar of the Tree of Life.

TRANSITION

A remedy to promote dying on any level in any way. Dying to the old and being reborn into the new.

Essential for this changing age and its changing energy. To help people through the destruction these changes require: environmental, personal global.

It can bring light, awareness and an ability to see where you have gone wrong, thus giving an opportunity for change.

Speeds up spiritual development.

Gatekeeper, doorkeeper remedy. Protects and then opens a door into another level of consciousness at the right time. Energy stored until right time comes and then facilitates the process enormously.

For major life transitions, birth and death.

Can be held over crown chakra as person is dying to help them leave peacefully.

HARD TO BE HERE

For delicate souls who are finding it difficult to withstand the harshness of some of our life on earth. Do not want to be here. Sleep or retreat out of it. Find it hard to be in a physical body and who keep drifting off.

For those stuck between the veils - so a limitless feeling of not being in one world or the other.

SHOCK

Where stress, shock, trauma have infiltrated all levels of consciousness and destroyed the beauty and resignation of the psyche.

Confusion over time from shock.

HEART CHAKRA & SADNESS

Profound effect on all levels of the Heart Centre.

Deep sadness, like a sea of sadness. Deep, unspoken, syphilitic grief.

Sadness about being bad.

Forsaken, abandoned, unloved. No peace, no sense of belonging. Disconnected and diffused.

Sadness closes down the Heart Chakra and all the layers of the Heart Chakra become so affected, it blocks grounding and inspiration. People who are so broken-hearted the Heart Centre closes, they cannot live, the light closes down.

Allows deep grief to be transmuted, not necessarily expressed.

Allows people to see what has been blocking heart.

Heavy-hearted with no motivation to make things better.

Patients would not present with this at all because are beyond
understanding they need help.

Lightens hearts weary and worn who cannot take any more.

Promotes group bonding on any level.

Facilitates speaking truth from the heart.

Sighing.

Heart pathology - angina. Heart attack. Fear and panic from thought of
it or even slight one.

THROAT CHAKRA

Affects communication on all levels, mental, emotional, physical and
spiritual.

Good for throat expression.

Helps people to become more sensitive and aware of the effect they can
have on others with their voice, to choose words carefully.

Lots of throat pathology, thyroid imbalance, especially overactive thyroid.

Aching in the throat.

UNWORTHINESS

Those who do well with their life's lessons but still feel unworthy and feel
they have not done well even, so therefore their psyche requests the
lesson over and over again for they do not believe in themselves.

They make life difficult for themselves and yet they are full of inner
beauty and potential.

Feel undeserving.

As if had done something wrong but not knowing what.

Fear of not being good enough, high expectations, external pressure to
perform well.

ANXIETY

For those with much fear, anxiety, stress.

Allows release of fear - fear of stepping into unknown spiritual areas or
areas that have been visited in previous lives and knowledge abused.

Rose

Remember fear and anxiety are about not trusting in God and in the process of life, incarnation.

Those who become prickly and hide, keep others away for they are so insecure and yet you see their inner beauty.

Fragility on all levels, not just a feeling of fragility on an emotional level as with Thuja, but a fragility as the individual has been worn down with anxieties.

For those who due to anxiety have turned too much to recreational drugs, smoking, drinking and allopathic medicine. They are seeking and seeking but working in darkness for they become deluded and actually more anxious.

Remedy is able to gently and slowly redress this balance, calming the anxiety an all levels.

CARERS

People worn down by years of caring for others.

People with a strong sense of duty and who have given their life to their family. Like Carcinosin they seem patient, sweet tempered and loving souls.

For therapists who deal with patients who are possessed and around whom there is a lot of negative energy.

Over-sentimental and over-sensitive: for example, to environmental issues. Over-anxiety, despair and sadness about the state of the environment.

WRONG PLACE

Tedium and getting stuck. Feel a bit cramped, in a shell.

As if in the wrong place. Stuck and confused.

Those who are seeking their path and feeling confused and they are at a cross-roads and do not really know what path to take.

Feeling unsettled.

SUPPORT

Remedy offers support, strength and security, like gentle but firm unquestioning parental love.

It is for the dark night of the soul; protective, supportive and stabilising in the midst of chaos.

Brings strength like Silica, strength, courage and determination.

Strengthens soul's will. Helps to see what must be done.

Good for spineless people (emotionally and spiritually). It helps them to grow and find their centre, purpose and stability.

CHILDREN & BABIES

Children who are somehow not allowed to grow up.

Children not listened to properly, fobbed off.

Materialistic children.

Helps children and mothers bond in unconditional love. Will find right connection to give them that love.

Helpful for new-born babies, to help settle them after a difficult journey and for the mother before she goes into labour or throughout labour.

To help heal stitches after an episiotomy and after Caesareans.

Helps mothers bring milk through at birth.

SPINE & BONES

Profound effect on the spine on all levels.

Crumbling spine. Bone spurs on spine. Trauma to spine.

Affects joints and bones and all diseases and distortions of them, leading to deformity and/or stunted growth.

Strong affinity with growth points of bone.

Arthritis and rheumatoid arthritis and the suppressed anger which has caused them.

As if bearing a weight and muscles feel strained. Skeleton, ribcage and skull especially.

EMOTIONAL

Brings great light, ease, joy, peace and tranquility. Gives detachment with clarity.

Anger, irritability, and a sense of being isolated and embattled. Lack of trust. Sense of separation.

Where there is havoc and chaos within families.

For those whose actions don't speak the truth. True feelings and emotions go on within. For those who hide, this remedy will break down the barriers.

For women who wear lots of perfume - hiding.

Rose

GENERAL

Works on many physical symptoms.

Relapsing complaints.

A great remedy for stunted growth: spiritual, emotional and physical.

Great weariness and physical depletion. Exhaustion. Adrenal energy very low.

For very stuck states, e.g. cancer, and rigidly ingrained thinkers.

Connection with cancer. A lot of grey in the aura.

Powerful remedy for the nervous system.

Very cold. Freezing. Coolness. Icy cold and shivering all over.

Sensitive to sun. Sunstroke.

Feeling hot and burning.

< 3.00pm

Hayfever.

Pituitary - Pill and HRT.

Splintering sensations.

Good for old injuries.

For old age.

PHYSICAL

Head: L side feels spongy. R side feels more compact.

Numb and heavy on R side.

Stiff from cerebellum round to front.

Sun headaches

Neck: neck as if crunching.

Sensations around the neck. A sense of disconnection.

Mouth: toothache, neuralgia in teeth and gums as if teeth are going to fall out.

Eye: remedy for the eyes - glaucoma, cataracts, clears vision.

Ear: pains R ear. Can't hear well.

Stomach: nausea throat and solar plexus.

Lungs: cleanses the lungs.

Chest weakness, problems: pneumonia, bronchitis, asthma.

Catarrh of the lungs. Tenacious and sticky. Lungs damaged by pollution.

Tar in the lungs. Smoking. Asthma.

Female: endometriosis, fibroids, polyps, heavy periods, difficult menopause, swollen breasts premenstrually.

Cystitis caused by suppressed anger and emotions.

Back: extremely cold down back.

Extremities: pain in L shoulder.

Helps energy flow from heart into hands.

Varicose veins, varicosities.

R big toe affected and balance.

Skin: can be used to focus on small issues like a laser e.g. warts and moles.

CONNECTIONS

Good for Virgos, emphasis on minute detail. Good for the pituitary.

Good with cranial osteopathy to unblock the sphenoid.

Image of crucifixion - rose growing up the cross and at its centre.

Pluto - felt had descended into a very dark place.

MIASMS

Very syphilitic.

Syphilitic destructiveness and greed, with an equally transformative power of light, with very strong protective powers.

Goes even beyond the syphilitic miasm, has a miasm of its own.

REMEDIES

Syphilinum. Tuberculinum. Phosphorus. Calc Phos. Ignatia. Causticum. Hypericum. Baryta Carb. Lycopodium. All colour remedies. Rainbow. Silica.

Suppression is at the centre of the remedy like Carcinosin.

Use with Clay and Oak for the lungs.

Antidoted by Peacock.

PRESCRIBING NOTES

Works more profoundly in high potencies, 1m and above.

Many elementals surround those given this remedy to lighten their load for fairy world is beginning to increase to help the planet.

Rose

It bears great repetition for it is much needed.
Very gentle almost ethereal in action but very strong and powerful.

Sandalwood Santalum album

T *he Sandalwood tree is native to southern Asia, but now grows mainly in the Mysore region of eastern India which includes the forests of Karnataka, Tamil Nadu and Kerala. It is an evergreen tree which grows to a height of 9 metres with leathery leaves and small purple flowers. The roots and heartwood which contain the essential oils take at least 15 years to develop, only reaching maturity after 60-80 years.*

Sandalwood has been part of the spiritual practice of ancient religions in the East since time immemorial. The wood is burnt as incense in temples, while the oil and paste are used in worship and have an important place in Aryuvedic, Tibetan and traditional Chinese medicines. Yogi masters use it to encourage the meditative state and to enhance devotion to God.

Sandalwood is one of the oldest known perfumery ingredients and was used as far back as the 5th century BC in India, Egypt and China. As a medicine it is valued for its anti-inlammatory, anti-febrile and antibiotic properties. Its bitter taste gives relief from problems of the throat, heart, lungs, gall bladder, stomach and genito-urinary system. Its oil is used for eczema and psoriasis. Emotionally it is used for hot agitated states that lead to headache, insomnia and nervous exhaustion, having a calming, tranquilising and relaxing effect.

Every Indian household also knows of the spiritual benefits of Sandalwood. The paste is applied to figures of the deities and used in almost all religious ceremonies either as incense or paste. It is applied to the dead, at least to the face, to carry the soul to the next life and is burnt on the funeral pyre.

ESOTERIC

Brings a treasure chest and presents you with the spirit of wisdom, wisdom in its purest form. It brings pure grace and reverence. Helps lead the individual to divine bliss.

Its smell enhances spiritual awareness and the awareness of elementals and angelic forces.

A pathfinder which will shine a light forward as well as backward.

Helps us get in touch with our spirituality.

Brings you to a point at which all is surrendered and all is gained, a point of stillness within.

Brings enlightenment but particularly through illusion and deception if not chaos and destruction.

Seeks and demands the highest motivation.

All lower selfish needs, motivations not coming from the heart will be destroyed.

A remedy for the meek and lowly, for the humble. The element of self-sacrifice in a good way.

Brings the ability to reduce the ego, to make it feel comfortable and secure so it can open and expand to the higher self. Humility will enter through trust in the divine and the higher self.

Remedy runs very deep into the past. It has the promise of renewal.

Passing of great ages of time. Sense of it just covering huge stretches of time.

Slows down time.

Balances the elements.

It represents the chaos of groups dissolving and reforming but always with the highest spiritual motivation.

CHAKRAS

For the Heart, Base and Crown Chakras and the movement between them.

For the polarity between the Crown and the Base.

Affects the cerebro-spinal fluid.

RESCUES

Excellent used in rescue and healing groups and circles for can facilitate easy rescues of souls long since passed.

Can also facilitate exorcism of trapped entities within the psyche. Surrounds entity with so much healing there is little trauma in the process. Gently removes these energies and brings them out with peace.

Very useful for cleansing layers of the aura.

ANCIENT RELIGION

Linked with true and ancient religion in its purest and most spiritual form.

Brings very deep, ancient information from long ago.

Connection through the remedy with disciples and saints and the energies they have represented through the ages.

Represents their thoughts, entities, quietness, ability to hold and support, to observe and to give simple, loving advice.

HEALING FOR GRIEF & TRAUMA

A great healing balm on all levels. It is balm for the hurt mind, body and spirit.

An excellent remedy for those who have been hurt in any way: physically, mentally or emotionally, especially if as result of hurt they begin to hide from the world or become reclusive. They do not want to participate for fear of being hurt again.

A remedy par excellence for grief for any reason. For those bereaved.

With great gentleness this remedy brings comfort, peace and rest to those who have been or who are going through crisis. It allows people to be aware that they are loved and supported even in the darkest hour. It brings sweetness out of bitterness, peace out of turmoil.

Brings peace, harmony where there is fear, shock and scatteredness of energies and emotions, as in the aftermath of explosions both physically and emotionally.

Situations which have taken people by surprise, where they feel shocked, betrayed and confused.

It can release fear and bring harmony and healing after any traumatic experience, birth or death.

Gives calmness, a point of being where nothing moves, and yet where everything can be observed and controlled.

Brings peace and tranquillity.

Good to be given to cast the individual back on themselves instead of questioning or blaming others or God for the events around them.

SPINE

Powerful connection with Jacob's Ladder, enabling powerful forces of light to move up and down the spine raising mortal consciousness to the light and bringing the light down to earth.

There is peace in the movement of energy through the spine. It brings consciousness of what is above and what is below.

Brings an energetically dead spine back to life.

BIRTH

A great balm remedy for all aspects of birth, death and transition states.

It is required for transitions to heal the upheavals that take place at these times.

Protects incoming spirits, especially those with fear of incarnation.

Will not hurt to give by rote in pregnancy for has a good calming effect on the incarnating spirit and on the mother, who often projects the wrong energy on to the soul while it is in womb.

It is about the birth process, the nurturing process of new life and bringing forth that which is hidden.

For the journey, the transformation, the transition of incarnating.

DEATH & DYING

Has a lot to do with death and the understanding of death.

Excellent if used as balm on dead bodies for it protects the spirit as it makes its transition to new state of consciousness.

It will take away the fear of death with the knowledge that there is no death but only life eternal.

Allows the easy transition of consciousness into the next state. Allows this whatever else is in the system. It will bring peace to the dying and enable death to take place in a state of awareness even through drugs.

For dying in shock - it will enable the soul to realise what has happened and to release the ties of the physical world.

Allows the seed atom in the Heart to work correctly at death.

Where a patient is dying but is still manipulating the death process with their negative life force for their own ends in a syphilitic manner. Remedy can release those around such a patient from the thrall of being drawn in. Give very frequently and spray around patient who is causing the disruption, for while they do this, they wish to take everyone else with them.

What we call death is the emergence or transition to another level and at each death there is something that passes upward and that which is discarded which passes downward. The passing upward is an increase in vibration and the passing downwards is a decrease. The rate of vibration translates for us into light and sound and space and time. This remedy helps the flow and puts us in touch with the rhythm.

INFLAMMATION

Great purifier and calms all kinds of inflammation on the very inner of the being, even inflammation at the auric level.

Inflammation: of spine, brain, in the tubes of the lungs, in the pericardium, of the central pillar of the body, of the urethra and bladder, of the throat.

Inflamed muscles, with tremendous soreness and stiffness.

Inflammation of the fallopian tubes and infertility. Pelvic inflammatory disease.

CANCER

Great healer of cancerous state and minds that have become cancerous.

Works also in cancerous states where fluids and toxins have become trapped in the physical body just before death. Remedy can ease this state greatly and facilitate easy transition.

Works better than morphine for pain is alleviated greatly.

Cancer especially of systems, e.g. lymph system.

HIGH BLOOD PRESSURE

This would be well considered as a high blood pressure remedy, especially that which goes up and down with no particular pattern. The remedy calms this markedly.

One of the major causes of high blood pressure that is so difficult to treat is the war between intellect and intuition.

Dangerously low blood pressure is the opposite fight and the remedy will work well in these cases also.

A fight goes on within Heart Chakra and Brow and higher centres.

EMOTIONAL

Weakness of the being or the aura. There is looseness, too much scatteredness and powerlessness about the person. Often the reaction is of anger, blaming others. Linked to Staphysagria.

Loss of sense of faith in myself.

Confusion over not knowing if had done any harm or done the right thing.

Boredom.

Sandalwood

GENERAL

In health, it brings greater connection on all levels.

Where with pathology there is isolation, numbness, withdrawal, lack of being able to communicate, to feel physically, emotionally and on a psychic level.

Nerves and nerve endings, the central nervous system.

Faintness.

Cleanses the lymph and cerebro-spinal fluid and balances the water element in the body. Corrects things that can be symptoms of imbalance in these elements, like inflammations and their emotional upheaval.

Blood cleanser, necessary whenever one is NBWS toxicity in the blood.

PHYSICAL

Head: dizzy in the head with sense of falling to the L.

Pain in the head on the L side.

Prickling and tingling sensation in the scalp, R sided on the inside of the head.

Eyes: sight problems, cataract, problems of not being able to sense the outside world.

R eye itching. Sensation of rock or grit in the eye.

Ear: R ear completely stopped - feeling unbalanced. Struggle to hear anything.

Pain L ear extending to L throat

Hearing problems, from congestion.

Nose: odours: of coal; sickly sweet; of putrefaction.

Helps all the senses.

Neck: prickling and tingling to the left of the neck, ear and throat.

Throat: thirst without dryness.

Painful but not sore throat.

Chest: oppression.

Heart: excellent remedy. For all traumas of the heart and blood pressure problems from whatever cause.

Can calm heart palpitations from whatever cause.

Pain in heart.

Stomach: nausea. Hiccups.

Urinary: inflammation of bladder and kidney.

Protein in urine. Toxaemia of pregnancy

Female: a short pulsing pain in the R ovary.

Back: pain at sacral level.

Severe lower back pain in many provers.

Ache L ribcage round spleen area. Fluttering in ribs.

R scapula aching as if the shoulder blade is much bigger with prickling and tingling.

Abdomen: felt bloated. Sulphuric flatulence.

Pain in the spleen area.

Twitch in groin on the L side.

Extremities: pain old injury R arm. Pain R shoulder.

Skin: for burns it has great use.

Balm for all sores on the skin.

CONNECTIONS

Spiral DNA.

There is some alignment with the alchemical role of Mercury.

With the silkworm as an example of receiving love and transforming it into the fine silver light which cocoons, heals and protects the etheric body but also links and suspends us within the universal consciousness. This keeps us connected and linked with universal love, bringing much protection and healing of fragments from shattering experiences which have left us bruised and broken.

With the Hebrew letters Aleph and Shin.

MIASMS

Goes very deep into the past and miasmatically, through the miasms down to the psoric idea of original sin, or original sin before the psoric miasm.

REMEDIES

Very safe to use with any other remedies.

Has great affinity to Iron Pyrites.

Grasses. Bamboo. Platina. Calc Carb and Oak. Phantom Quartz.

Sandalwood

PRESCRIBING NOTES

Can be used in conjunction with colour remedies to clear blocks and seal the aura.

Works well topically as cream or lotion.

Patients taking the remedy will often experience sleepiness as it relaxes those very tight and tense parts of the system which have forgotten how to relax and have become worn down by the traumas of life.

[Remedy can be put on the body after death at the crown or on the heart. Ed]

Sapphire

*T*here are many colours of sapphire but the most common is blue and this is the colour of the crystal used to make this remedy. Sapphires are known as stones of wisdom, each colour having its own particular alignment. Blue sapphire particularly stimulates seeking after truth and is very grounding and calming. According to Buddhists, Sapphire stimulates a desire for prayer, devotion, spiritual enlightenment and inner peace. In ayurvedic medicine it is used to treat colic, rheumatism and mental illness. It is also said to work as an antidepressant and to open the heart. It aids the digestive system and the pituitary gland and through the pituitary balances the whole of the endocrine system. It amplifies thoughts, clairvoyance and astral projection and communication with angels and guides. It opens the Throat Chakra and stimulates communication on all levels. Sapphire can rid the mind of unwanted thoughts bringing joy, beauty and tranquility. Sapphire has been called 'a stone of prosperity' as it can sustain the gifts of life, eliminate frustration, and fulfill dreams and desires.

ESOTERIC

It is very grounding and earthing and enables you to stay stable while working with the highest energies. It reaches into the depths of the being while keeping people grounded.

Removes lower frequency energy.

Removes blocks at the lower level, which frees, opens, expands the mind, so potential can be realised. When blocks are removed there is an increase of creativity and energy and the Brow Chakra is released.

Blockages in the lower three chakras and within the lower level of energy within the aura inhibit the soul's aspiration and vision and consciousness in how it can see its way into the light.

It removes blocks that are stopping you moving forward and allows you to receive the new energy to the best of your ability.

The karmic blueprint is changed, knots untied, primarily in the lower chakras and within the emotional body. For it is these that hold back the individual and prevent movement into the light.

It helps many lost and stuck souls to be healed.

Removes lies, untruths, things that aren't true, not necessarily lies that have been told but things that no longer resonate with your truth and with your higher purpose.

CHAKRAS

Grounding in its effect.

Energy moving downward from Throat to Sacral Chakra.

Works from higher levels down very quickly, takes energy down the chakras and down the body to whatever area is creating a blockage in energy and clears it.

Fundamentally a remedy for opening the Crown, Brow and Throat. But this can't happen while there are still knots lower down and the remedy releases these.

Intimately connected with the karmic blueprint of each individual and has a profound effect on the Thymus.

Opens the Crown Chakra.

SOLAR PLEXUS

Cleanses the astral body and the Solar Plexus.

It works in particular on the Solar Plexus and all the organs of the Solar Plexus and the emotional body and emotional energy. Heals the spleen in particular. Limitations on energy that have been held onto for a long time are released.

Enables better use of prana through the breath.

The release of the Solar Plexus enables the Heart to open and energy to move up the spine and into the Throat.

It has a profound effect on the balance between the Throat Chakra and the Solar Plexus Chakra.

THROAT

Affects the parathyroid.

Throat and communication. The unspoken word affecting the pancreas and the Throat needing to be released so the pancreas can function properly.

Deep grief and sadness held in the throat. The remedy goes beyond, underneath and behind Nat Mur where Nat Mur is indicated and doesn't work, when grief is locked in the throat, even more so with Ignatia.

As if choking from something stuck in the throat.

Not feeling worthy, good enough.

Sins of omission, not having said what you knew to be true.

GENERAL
Regulates the metabolism.
Connects the thyroid and digestive energy.

PHYSICAL
Kidneys: profound effect on the kidneys. Can be used especially for recurrent kidney problems which are connected intimately to the karmic blueprint and the issues the soul has to deal with in the incarnation.
Thymus: burning and aching.
Stomach: rumbling and gurgling.
Extremities: tingling in the hands.

CONNECTIONS
Violet and purple light.

REMEDIES
Red. Diamond.

PRESCRIBING NOTES
It has a profound effect when used as an essence and as a remedy needs to be used in the higher potencies.
One of the best remedies to use for people who do not respond to indicated remedies as it removes blocks to the way forward.
This is one of the most self adjusting of the new remedies.
This is a remedy which will be greatly needed in the future and there is much more information on its healing to be brought forward. The information we have now is only what is needed for the present.

Selenite

S elenite is the crystalline form of gypsum (which is the remedy Ca. Sulph). It is found in the form of colourless, white or even greenish lon tubular or needle-like crystals. The crystal looks hard but is actually qui. fragile and breaks into shards easily. Light travels along the lengths of th crystal easily. Its name derives from Selene, the Greek Moon godess and . has always been associated with the female moon energies. It was eve. thought to wax and wane as the moon did. Pliny wrote that beehives use. to be made of it so that people could watch the bees at work; it was used b the ancients as we might use glass as it can be split into thin sheets. Seleni. was regarded as an attractor of love and a stone to restore harmony betwee. quarrelling lovers. It could also increase the power of the imagination. It . said to provide access to past and future lives and to give mental clarit. helping with the ability to make judgements and resolve disputes. . decreases reticence and promotes successful business dealings. It can hel. with problems caused by dental amalgam in the body and with free radica. toxicity. It is also said to be able to promote cell regeneration and extend th lifespan. It promotes flexibility of the spine and muscles and is good for an. disorder of the skeletal structure.

This remedy has had two provings, both blind. In one, all of the si. women provers experienced the same lost, indifferent and out of body stat. described below. It is very unusual in a proving for all of the provers t. experience exactly the same state.

ESOTERIC

Dying, sense of peace, connecting what is above and what is below. Allowing babies peace on that side of transition and allowing a peacefu. death.

May take the person back to the time when they were born when they took their first breath, help them to balance that first breath, help them move on karmically.

A remedy of great peace and power.

It has the ability to make a connection between heaven and earth - bring light down. It's about aspiration.

Given to the mother it will pass to the child, help the child to be happier to be incarnated so that the baby's soul integrates into the physical body more easily.

CHAKRAS

It is a remedy for the Base, the Throat, the Parathyroid and the Crown Chakras.

Affects the higher chakras.

A lot of activity round the Third Eye.

OUT OF THE BODY

Profound out of body states. Lost souls.

People who do not want to be here, withdrawn, in their own world, cut off. Floaty and gone. An effort to focus on anything.

Disembodied. Feel as if lost, surrounded by swirling mists, but nowhere, just lost. A wraith. I want to cry, but can't, don't have a body to cry with.

Feeling of being cut off, separated, pulled out, in a cocoon, drawn out, wanting to whizz off into space but being drawn back again.

Felt as if I'd been in a cloud, round the head and shoulders. As if asleep. Profoundly tired, closing the eyes, going to sleep into a dream. Can't wake up. So tired, lethargic, heavy. Heavy weight on top of my head. No energy.

Can't be bothered, shut off. Not wanting to do anything. Haven't got the energy to cry.

Totally cut off and indifferent. Can't react to anything and don't want to. Want to shut down and shut off.

As though something has happened to the emotions; can't experience joy. Can't experience any emotions at all, not pleasant. Not in touch with my emotions, just lost.

As if encased in something rubbery, something soft but resistant. As if nothing can get in or out. Feel closed in, entombed.

Swearing.

Still, detached in a very positive way, no longer affected by human desires. Able to step outside. The remedy gives detachment. It helps us to step back from our emotions. For when emotions are too intense, caught up in maelstrom of emotions, To give detachment and calm them.

A pleasant state of being cut off but floating peacefully in one's own world - happily detached, far removed from cares. Feel very safe, wrapped up in cotton wool.

Sense of floating, being comfortably disconnected.

EFFECTS OF PRESCRIBED DRUGS

This is a remedy for people given Prozac and other antidepressants. They are lost, sad, indifferent and don't know it. They may be fine on the outside, on the inside lost in their mist, shut out from themselves. Truly a remedy for lost ones.

Bland state of nothing in particular - no emotions, no spiritual contact - a blanket around me preventing anything coming through. Reminded of how I was when I took the Pill in my 20s: coming off was like having a grey wooly blanket taken out of my head. This is like having that blanket back.

Those on antidepressants and tranquillisers, psychiatric drugs.

Lost outer edges of body, as if in warm water. Don't know where body ends. Not pleasant, as if on drugs, can't do anything about it.

Remedy for suppression - really subtle, they don't know they're suppressed.

POOR THINKING

Inability to talk - stupid. Can't be bothered to try, give up easily.

Can't think logically.

Had a sentence and seconds later couldn't remember it. Said something and can't remember what I'd said.

It will help people who cannot thing straight, help confusion, backward children, children who are slow, who just can't think - anybody, any stage of life where this is the case, e.g. menopause.

A great aid for clarifying the mind. Gets rid of detritus in the corners of our minds. May be hard because it is easy to hide behind muddled thoughts.

Can bring great peace to a troubled mind, acceptance of problems in life, an opportunity for the spirit to do what it has come to do. Will help a mind that cannot rest because of material concerns.

Helps us to be more intuitive and less wordy.

Helps people refine their thoughts, aspire to higher things.

For rigid thinking, someone who can't get out of thinking in a straight line.

MILK, CALCIUM AND BONES

Big connection with milk.

Excellent remedy for lactation, for the post-partum period.

Breast feeding mothers. First time mothers where there is a strong bond between mother and baby but the practical things are not instinctive.

For weaning - again to help the mother's milk supply adjust to the baby's needs.

Affinity with the parathyroid and calcium balance with the body. For teeth and bones.

Weakness of the bone structure like Calc Phos. Protection against osteoporosis. Good for osteoporosis, general brittleness and fragility, will give strength.

WOMEN

A powerful female remedy.

It is helpful for mothers especially when the children are leaving home, the empty nest syndrome.

Painful menses, copious flow, when this is weakening and draining the woman especially around the menopause and post-partum. It will also bring the cycle in tune with the phases of the moon.

In later life it will help the woman to be in contact with her intuitive side.

Period pains outside the menses.

EMOTIONAL

Emotional people with their intuitive side blocked and their breathing affected.

It can unburden the person of excess emotional baggage.

It will bring peace.

Those who lack the courage of their convictions.

Gives acceptance of a problem without struggle rather than submission to it.

The remedy can bring peace and tranquility. A sense of peace, trust, of being carried.

A remedy for depression - the sort of depression where you don't want to come out of it. Stuck feeling. There is no light so don't look for it. A very heavy energy round the remedy.

GENERAL

People who lack stamina - soft where they ought to be firm.

Strong effect on the hypothalamus and pituitary - about growth and development, children who fail to grow upward in stature - close to Silica.

Useful for babies born too quickly or who have been stuck, not wanting to be born, cry all the time, do not want to be put down, unsettled.

Tingling throughout the body.

Incredible coldness, especially the site of old lower back injuries.

A profound effect on all spinal energy, and the cerebro-spinal fluid. Will help babies and children having cranial osteopathy for it to work much deeper.

Affects the water balance in the body.

Jet lag.

For old people.

PHYSICAL

Head: headache. Compression on the head round the temples. Affects the pineal gland.

Neck: pain down right side of neck and stiffness.

Mouth: ulcers.

Throat: a lot of catarrh in throat. Thick white catarrh like Kali Mur. Post-nasal catarrh.

Dreadful aching in the throat.

Stomach: severe nausea. Travel sickness. Acid stomach from mind churning.

Lungs: Silicosis. Pneumoconiosis. Helps to balance the breath. Asthma from anxiety. Coal miners' diseases. Can't breathe, choked with catarrh.

Extremities: restless and fidgety, legs and buttocks very uncomfortable.

Bones of hands aching < pressure. Hands going hot and cold.

CONNECTIONS

Beneath the connection with the moon and water is a connection with fire and Kundalini energy, spiritual fire, Kundalini fire.

The colours blue and green, aqua, silvery blue.

It will help to undo some of the damage of fluoride.

MIASMS

This is quite a syphilitic remedy - fragile, soft bones, bones that don't grow, bone diseases, early tooth decay, soft teeth.

REMEDIES

Phosphorus. Silica. Lac Humanum. Phos Ac. Granite. Opium. Luna. Calc Carb.

late - damage done to Brow Centre by vaccination.

PRESCRIBING NOTES

In low potency it will increase the milk supply in nursing mothers. In 30c it will regulate an over abundance of milk.

Silver Birch Betula pendula

T he birch is a pioneer - it was the first tree to colonise Europe as the ic melted at the end of the last Ice Age and it is the first tree to grow in poor soil, for example after plantations of pine have been cleared. Indeed i grows best in poor, sandy, gravelly soil. It is the hardiest of all the broadlea trees, and its fallen leaves and timber and the nitrogen fixing nodules in it roots fertilise the soil and enable larger trees to grow. It is a small, open tre with a short life span, rarely living for more than 80 years, but it grou quickly and produces tiny seeds in huge numbers, so has the ability t regenerate derelict areas rapidly. Conservationists and foresters can see it a a nuisance because it can be so invasive. The bark is waterproof and encourages the growth of fungus especially fly agaric, but the birch is one o the few trees which burns well while still alive. The timber is not valued commercially as it decays very easily. Wine is still produced from the swee sap tapped from the tree in the spring, particularly in Scandinavia.

It is a graceful, light and airy tree having a feminine energy, ofter known as 'The Lady of the Woods'. In Norse mythology it is the tre associated with Frigga, Odin's wife, who was the goddess of married love the sky and the clouds. The twigs of the tree have been associated with cleansing and mortification and were used prosaically in brooms and mor painfully for the mortification of the flesh and the punishment o disobedient children. They were also used for beating evil spirits out o lunatics and for the annual 'beating the bounds' to maintain establishea boundaries between parishes. The sap and bark have both been used fo healing as a diuretic, antiseptic and tonic.

ESOTERIC

A remedy of magnificent beauty and love. Re-establishes love and harmony where it has been lost from the soul. It is refined, gentle and powerful. It breathes and attracts light. Gives an understanding of how the breath of God gives life.

Brings the Christ vibration.

Brings great increased connection to the guides.

It is a profound rescuer of trapped souls. Those with open auras, those who have abused themselves with recreational drugs can be brought back and rescued safely with the healing powers of this remedy.

Use when lower astral entities get close and try to throw you off course - which is what happens when those with drug experiences do not know themselves. They listen to lower astral forces and become confused as to what is theirs and what is not.

Facilitates safe exploration of the astral plane so you may feel out of the body, disorientated, sleepy and blank and yet within this, a sense of peacefulness and safety. Restlessness occurs when you become aware of where you are.

It enables you to go into deep dark realms safely.

A beneficial remedy for those people who go to psychics and mediums for their decision making. They do not take responsibility for own karma. It is good to listen but always follow advice within. Remember, all mediums who smoke are subject to lower astral entities giving them wrong information.

CHAKRAS

Has profound effect on Throat, Heart and Crown Centres.

Profound effect on the Throat Centre; removes the blockages preventing energies rising to head. Opens the ears to the silence in which the divine word can be heard, opens the ears to receiving the wisdom from the guides.

Powerful remedy for the birth of the higher creative self through the Throat.

Links the Crown and Base chakras particularly.

Good Saturn (Base) quality. Opens the Heart and it with the pineal gland. Through this you gain the vision of your own true effulgent individuality.

Creates healing and holiness and protection of the head centres.

ELEMENTALS

The tree produces it own song. It is connected to etheric angelic beings, tree beings and fairies. It is a tree of magic and protection, for it harmonises, heals, balances and protects all other trees. It listens to their troubles and unburdens. Woodland animals can be healed by its power.

The remedy has great healing power for all living things including the earth itself; can heal the atmosphere, even holes in the ozone.

Gives much healing to nature; redresses the balance, brings back equilibrium to elementals so traumatised by what man is doing to the planet they cannot do their work properly.

RELEASE OF KARMA

Karmic states where people have been broken down, pushed to the limits, there is no more to give, reaching breaking point. Fear, weariness and injury, which have come from being battered in so many previous lives.

It ends karmic issues where you or your patients reach a point where you think you cannot go on, where you do not think you can suffer or learn anymore, where there might be utter despair and exhaustion, where you simply feel you cannot function anymore. It is in the night of darkness of despair that the light floods in and transformation - so called miracles - happen and people's lives and souls are transformed.

Good for those who toil and toil and toil and feel not worthy themselves. Those who find it difficult to release burdens, who feel unworthy. Lightens heavy karmic loads. It enables you to channel light beings who do not bring forth messages. It brings joy and laughter.

Helps change the experiences so we do not repeat the same karmic or emotional pattern.

For all karma relating to blood letting, killing and mass murder and death through violence. Utter despair after killing, realise its futility.

Can reveal karmic connections between members of families and will allow you to see where the patient's block is with another member of their family.

Healer of wounds of all sorts including spiritual and karmic wounds incurred over lifetimes.

Expansive vibration and its aura spreads over a wide net of vibration and pulls many thoughts and entities into its centre to offer them up for healing and transformation, even those thought patterns and karmic patterns which are reluctant to move on.

RELEASE OF PAIN & BURDENS

Has magical powers of transformation. Past, present and future blocks can be ameliorated by its energy.

It lightens the load, offers the lighter side of life, a funnier, lighter choice. Helps to attract lightness and bring it into people's lives.

For years of hurt and grief, years of crying, open emotional wounds.

Releases and lets go some of the old hurt, so allowing more freedom of choice.

Brings out grief locked in the Throat Centre: from wrong-doing, over things which have done harm or caused death, things which have destroyed love. This grief inhibits true energy of the Throat.

Works well on tortured souls; those who have been so deeply hurt that they have retreated from their body. Releases old grudges and enables the heart to sing.

Allows inner flexing and opening and closing, releasing worries, fears, shocks, griefs.

STRESS & RELAXATION

Many traumas pass through its energy fields and it is capable of releasing much trauma, particularly emotional.

Brings peace, tranquility and relaxation in states of burnout, overactivity, overwork - a remedy for people living in crisis situations: epidemics, wars, natural disasters, practices that are too busy! An occasional dose will help people keep going, but with gentleness.

When you are faced with a challenge: the point before breaking through into the transformation of light.

For a fragile nervous system no longer coping with the changes asked of it, causing nervous disorders, even insanity states; brings spiritual and psychic strength and stability.

Helps change, letting go, moving on, going round and round the spiral, collecting knowledge, experiences.

Brings release.

For now, when everything is speeding up. Where time is constantly spoken about in the sense of there not being enough of it. Enables us to relax and achieve our goals with calm.

Disturbances of sleep patterns, cannot release and relax into spiritual life of night. Good given at night to help ease the cares of the day.

Restless physically. For people who need to relax and find it difficult. Restless and impatient, cannot get comfortable, bordering on irritation.

Rigidity. Keeps stasis from building up and helps the balance between stillness and activity.

PURIFICATION

It has profound, magical healing effects and purifies very deeply. Purifies and harmonises.

Has an affinity with the kidneys and to the skin, works on fluidity and restores the correct balance of fluids within the body. Purifies body fluids.

Burns away the dross. Not quite safe to give it when there is a lot of pathology because of this quality.

Another remedy to be added to the water - connected with clearing radiation especially.

MASCULINE/FEMININE ENERGIES

Strong effect on sexual energy, helping you to use it in the correct manner and to enjoy sexual experience in the way God meant it to be enjoyed, for if this power is used correctly you can travel into realms of healing and power. This remedy can rectify any imbalance here and also bring morality back.

It is steadfast, strong, but light. It has a strong affinity to the moon and feminine energy and Venus has a close connection to its power.

Releases and balances female energy where this has been suppressed and denied.

connected with male and female energies combined in the head and in the physical body and all becomes one. It gives us a glimpse of the unity that is.

WEAKNESS

Complete exhaustion, wiped out. No kidney energy. Can't be bothered. Incredibly tired. Heaviness and sleepiness. Great relaxation. As if lazy.

Weakness of all systems, especially of the etheric body, nervous system and Crown Chakra.

Trembly and weak.

CHILDREN

For teenagers and all children where the destructive element is strong, where there may be possession.

For the children born as a result of genetic engineering and artificial fertilisation procedures.

Important to give to children of IVF and to help women who are put on fertility drugs and to make up their minds whether they really want to go through that process or not.

MENTAL

Cannot concentrate. Mind scattered. Blankness.

Insanity - swearing, hissing, congenital. Catatonic states.

Gives detachment.

Those who can only see black and white, no greys.

GENERAL

Stuck, almost like Clay. Unblocks all the channels on all levels.

Brings stabilisation and consolidation. Helps people to put down their roots, helps to firm their resolve.

Water balance.

Rebalances the pituitary and the other endocrine glands after the pill and HRT.

TB of the lungs, glands and where TB has caused damage to organs of the Sacral Centre. Also where TB has been caused by vaccination or immune system breakdown.

Support remedy for autoimmune illnesses. Boosts the immune system. Can be used very well with Echinacea, and here might work better in tincture form.

PHYSICAL

Head: headache. R sided headache.

Ears: hardness of hearing.

Throat: sore throats.

Lungs: shortness of breath. Cyanosis. Lung cancer and smokers. Allergies like hay fever < later spring/early summer.

Stomach: sensation of a ball in the solar plexus. Nausea.

Kidneys: powerful effect on kidneys and water balance, purification and adrenal energy.

It can easily, but easily, dissolve kidney stones and allow kidneys to breathe. Allows individual to express themselves more.

Pain R kidney.

Female: fertility and female gynaecological problems. For menstrual irregularities particularly insufficiency of menstruation. Dysmenorrhea.

Physical birth. Contractions too painful or insufficient, where the baby has come so far and the process stops.

Abdomen: Crohn's disease.

Back: pain R side between shoulder blade and spine and R kidney pain. Sensation of a weight on the back.

Skin: a balm made from bark of this tree has great antiseptic properties. Used on any skin condition, it purifies and lightens the vibration, brings back life. You will use this remedy much. Peeling, desquamation, dry, scaling. Removes toxins, allowing the tissues to heal.

Silver Birch

MIASMS

Tendency to withdraw - Syphilitic element.

Tubercular.

REMEDIES

Related to Silverfish and Woodsmoke.

Close to Red Chestnut.

Trilogy of Buddleia/Silver Birch/Oak.

Female counterpart to Oak.

For people who are constantly on the go, restless, fidgety, like Zinc, Medorrhinum, Syphilinum, Tuberculinum and Copper Beech.

Slate (Cumbrian)

S*late is a metamorphic rock that is formed from pre-existing rocks or mudstone due to changes in temperature, pressure, stress or chemistry. Its age is not specific and depends on where it is found and its history, but roughly between 350 and 500 million years. It is usually found in veins between other types of rock. The slate for this remedy came from Cumbria.*

Over 650 million years ago, in the absence of vegetation and with great extremes of temperature, the existing sedimentary rocks were rapidly broken down into boulders and stones small enough to be carried away by the fast flowing waters shed from the hills. Particulate material, breaking continuously into finer and finer particles as it travelled, was eventually deposited as silt and mud on the bed of the shallow sea. Then about 500 million years ago, extensive land movements took place during which great folding of the shallow sea deposits occurred. The concertina effect of this folding created enormous pressure in the layers of mud, compressing and heating the deposits until they were converted into slate rock.

Slate is considered the lowest grade of metamorphic rock. It is intermediate in hardness between mica schists and shale, which consists of compacted clay or mud. It is a fine-grained brittle rock which splits readily into thin smooth-faced layers or sheets used as paving slabs or roofing tiles. Blackboards and handheld writing tablets were once made of slate, and the name of the rock has become the name of the tablets themselves. It tends to split and crumble easily when worked and there is a lot of wastage when it is trimmed. Slates are generally dark blue-grey, green or black in colour, but may also be red or brown depending on the original rocks from which they were formed and their mineral content.

The nature of the mining for slate has depended on where it is found, but much has been open cast, leaving huge spoil heaps and open quarries blighting the landscape. There is little mining of slate now, but anyone who has visited the old slate mining villages can attest to the sense of weight and depression surrounding them.

ESOTERIC

Lot of darkness in this remedy. A remedy for very heavy states.

A remedy for this century. Very powerful.

Very purifying, cleansing.

Breaks through old patterns, karmic patterns. Releases ancestral karma.
Important for ancestors.

Gives great protection on both a physical and spiritual level.

Slate

Protects from violent male influences.

The energy that is released by the remedy is a soft feminine, lunar energy - emotional, reflective and kindly - it brings much kindness. Yin.

An affinity with water.

CHAKRAS

All chakras especially Heart and Thymus.

Throat, Sacral, Crown, Brow, Parathyroid, Base Chakras.

TRANSITIONS

Transitional states - useful for shifting from one form to another.

A metamorphosis from one state to another.

Can bring about movement on all levels where things are stuck.

SPLIT & CUT OFF

Like Thuja splits in personality with separation of soul and body.

Split like Anacardium.

Contradictions, contradictory states.

Sensation of a cocoon of slate round the heart, encased in slate, cut off (c.f. Berlin Wall).

People who need this remedy are very closed as if encased. Surrounded by a wall and cannot break through.

Cut off from others, a kind of solidifying, away from others.

It promotes brotherhood and helps to heal people who feel separated.

Coldness on right, heat on left, expansion, lightness on right, contraction left.

Right able to move, heightened, fine awareness. Left - clay, deadened, heavy.

Where there is no will, no contact with others.

HEART

Great heaviness around heart, throat, thymus.

Intensity of the pain so great that the heart has closed down and the light gone out of people's lives.

Remedy for the heart where great grief and sadness has hardened the heart and prevented them giving or receiving love. Similar to Nat Mur.

Much heartache involved.

It releases an enormous amount of pain deep in the thymus and heart.

Allows the heart to open to love - being open to and able to receive love. All negative influences can be removed.

Deep depression with a sense of no way out at all. Very, very dark moods.

Hopelessness and despair, being trapped on a physical level, losing direction.

RIGIDITY

Very rigid in thinking. Remedy helps break down rigidity, fixed ideas - helps people to see more clearly. To see the light of new situations.

Strongly superstitious and fixed.

People trapped in never ending circles and cannot see a way forward.

Feel dead, like a blob.

NEGATIVE & MATERIALISTIC

Critical and dismissive. Dissatisfied. Opinionated. Sarcastic.

Religious haughtiness.

Haughtiness but behind it a lot of fear and insecurity. Fear that others will see their true selves.

A feeling of dirtiness, unworthiness, like Thuja.

Achieving the goal is everything. Driven. Those who will achieve ambition at all costs.

For the thrusting smoothie, male energy, possibly psychopathic.

No feeling for those trodden on.

Demanding, selfish.

Petty minded.

MENTAL ILLNESS

Possibly psychopathic tendencies, with lack of remorse.

Stormy, negative states, extreme alternating moods.

Mentally deficient - unable to express oneself.

Very hard to keep still, rocking but not manic. People who are very disturbed.

Difficulty staying present. A tendency to drift off and disappear.

Unnatural gaiety - laughing.

Complete detachment and calm.

Kind of loss of will - no desires, not even for food.

FEAR

Lot of darkness and fear. Fear of looking into that darkness. Fear of what might be revealed within them.

Darkness and fear of what will happen in future prevents them from looking sideways.

Can only look forward but blinkered.

DECEPTION

There is no strength to this remedy. It masquerades as being strong but isn't. Acquires strength through deception.

For very unpleasant, syphilitic states - there is a sweet nastiness, a deceiving.

Deception.

Those who lie and cheat.

For those where things are not what they seem.

Helps reveal the true colours of person.

ANGER

Very angry. Anger at injustice. Anger over vaccination.

Desire for revenge, to punish.

Desire to reveal evil.

CHILDREN

A great children's remedy.

For children in pain, suffering.

For the Brow Centre in children and the pituitary.

All our children need this now because they have been vaccinated. For vaccinated children who cannot fulfill their purpose because of the damage.

Puny children. Children with bones growing, nutritional problems, malnourished children.

For problems assimilating on a physical level and assimilating life's lessons.

Crumbling bones and bone problems in children.

Children with learning difficulties. Loss of memory for words. Dyslexic, difficult to write and spell.

Protects the embryo - perhaps remedy would go back in time to when conception takes place.

For babies conceived outside the uterus. Where remedies do not work this will reveal what is going on. A major remedy for children conceived outside the womb or by a.i. - no human matrix, absence of emotion, almost frightening. The unpleasantness of what is hidden. A really nasty softness to it.

Where birth is a struggle. Remedy can help and ease birth. Relaxes baby and mother.

Infertility. Failure to ovulate in women. Low sperm count in men.

Remedy affects the pituitary.

NERVOUS SYSTEM

The focus of pathology for this remedy. Not cancerous.

Nerve sensation either deadened or heightened.

Sensitivity to noise: seems loud and intrusive, noise of writing became deafening.

Numbness and tingling down R side.

Trembling inside.

Body jerking -R side. Jerking was stopping and starting suddenly.

Started rocking and could not stop.

Alzheimer's. M.S.

Nervous system symptoms like Alumina.

GENERAL

Strongly R sided.

Very, very cold.

Extreme coldness with nausea or violent vomiting.

Injuries that take a long time to heal, cuts.

Stopped states - such as amenorrhoea.

Heaviness and constriction.

Advanced states of pathology: near death.

Slate

PHYSICAL

Head: R sided head pain.

   Headaches R side of occiput. May extend over R eye.

   Back of the head, occiput affected by the remedy.

   Affinity for the pineal gland, hypothalamus.

   Could be useful for brain tumours.

Eyes: affects eyes and vision particularly. Eye injuries. The inner eye. Pains in the R eye. Irritation.

Ears: excruciating pain R ear and R eye.

Throat: tickling in throat coming and going.

Neck: heaviness around neck and shoulders and tightness back of neck.

Pancreas: diabetes.

Heart: affinity for Heart Centre, physical heart, circulatory system, lymphatic system, blood.

   Helps circulation of blood and its oxygenation.

Lungs: for those who cannot breathe easily.

Spine: ankylosing spondylitis. Especially R side of shoulder and neck area.

Tissue: gangrenous and necrotic states very strong.

Extremities: cold feet.

CONNECTIONS

The Doctrine of Signatures is important for this remedy.

Connection with Minerva, Artemis, Athene and owls.

Triangular relationships.

Images: skyscrapers made of slate. Red, white, black. Triangles.

MIASMS

A deeply syphilitic remedy.

Very tubercular because of a great need for freedom in their psyche.

REMEDIES

Sulphur. Clay. Silica. Tin. Mimosa. Thuja. Berlin Wall. Anacardium. Baryta Carb.

Syphilinum. Jet.

Snowdrop Galanthus nivalis

This is the common Snowdrop now found in huge numbers in woods and on banks throughout Britain. Now widespread, snowdrops were once quite rare in Britain, and were found only in damp woodlands in England. There is even some doubt as to whether they are native or naturalised from the continent - the earliest mention of them growing in the wild was not until 1770. Now they grow almost anywhere in the British Isles, but they are especially well suited to limestone terrain such as is found in the Cotswolds. They prefer dappled shade and cannot stand the bulbs becoming too warm or dried out, so are rarely found in open pastures. There are 19 wild species in the genus Galanthus, a member of the Amaryllis family, found from Spain to the Caucasus, with most growing in Turkey. Many of the varieties which have naturalised in Britain were brought back here from Russia by soldiers returning from the Crimean War.

The snowdrop is a bulbous perennial with narrow strap-shaped blue-green leaves. The flowers are always white - the name Galanthus means 'milk flower' - and are unscented. They hang down singly and have a green V shaped mark towards the tip of the inner petals. Sometimes the flowers are double. The flowers close at night and open in the morning to attract the early insects. The snowdrop is undergoing a revival with over 600 varieties now available and more appearing every year. The bulbs mutate and hybridise very easily, leading to many new cultivars. As with tulipmania in the 17th century, bulbs can change hands for very high prices.

Snowdrops are flowers of hope and courage, a sign that winter will soon come to an end and spring is on the way. Despite their apparent delicacy, they are quite robust, withstanding wind and rain, ice and snow. They were connected with the Virgin Mary because of the purity of their whiteness and hence to the Christian festival of Candlemas (the Purification of Mary) on February 2nd. In some areas, girls would wear a snowdrop as a symbol of virginity and purity. Wearing the flowers is said to bless you with pure and lofty thoughts, perhaps because of this association with the Feast of the Purification. They were linked with death and sorrow and considered an omen of death, perhaps because their heads were reminiscent of shrouds, and so were often planted in graveyards. It may be because of this that it was considered unlucky to bring them into the house. Bringing a single snowdrop into a house was believed to portend that a member of the household would die before the following spring, although some say bringing in a handful is not unlucky. According to one superstition, to bring

Snowdrop

snowdrops into the home before Valentine's Day meant you would miss out on any chance of marrying that year. For some, the snowdrop was meant to represent "the passing of sorrow".

In Anthroposophy, all plants are images of the soul world and all spring flowers connected with the gesture of longing. Flowers open in a sequence which represents the strengthening of the sun in the sky and the symbolic sun in the heart. Snowdrop represents what in your own soul is at the beginning of awakening and is said to awaken the soul. It is a moonflower, bridging the change from the darkness of the night into the light of day. The snowdrop flower turns away from the sun to face down into the stored warmth and light of the previous year, spiritually drawing the sun out of the earth. The next flower to bloom, the crocus, holds this light and warmth as if between hands cupped in prayer. Daffodils then broadcast this light in many directions. Leaves also indicate this development, beginning as simple strap shaped leaves with the first flowers in early spring, becoming more complex as the power of the sun grows through the year.

The flowers for this remedy were growing among the roots of a lime tree and were seen to be surrounded by fairies who were singing.

ESOTERIC

Reaches the gold and silver vibration to give a life-line into light. Ray of blue and violet.

Strong spiritual energy.

Helps soul to leave body and see its state in relation to the physical, from a distance.

Allows communication with the invisible world. Helps to develop intuition and trust in it.

Gives faith and confidence of our links with spiritual world.

Useful for souls lost and in despair to help them connect with Source.

Helps psychic and clairvoyant development.

Promotes astral travel.

Allows you to see yourself with detachment.

Has a steadfast, resilient and stubborn power of healing: ensures great healing.

Its energy is hidden but it can bring in great light.

Facilitates clearing, cleansing and purification on all levels and allows you to become true healer.

Allows all energies to flow harmoniously.

Strong etheric healer.

One of the best remedies for healing heart and mind.

All subtle bodies are separate and floating - remedy gives grounding and centering.

Floatiness, disjointed out-of-the body feelings.

CHAKRAS

Acts on Brow and Crown.

Awakens all chakras esp. Heart and Crown.

Links Sacral, Throat and Crown.

Crown Chakra, link between heaven and earth.

SHOCK & TRAUMA

Clears deep shock and trauma.

Heals subtle damage of shock and trauma. Refines and purifies etheric structures.

Abortion and miscarriage - heals mother and incoming soul before and after. Removes trauma from incoming soul so can incarnate again.

FEAR, ANXIETY & LACK OF CONFIDENCE

For fear, trauma, those facing unfamiliar things, fear of change.

Fragility, fear of manifestation, anxiety in coping with life and its challenges.

Image of someone getting smaller and smaller going down a tunnel unable to see the light, feeling alone and disconnected from everyone.

Frightened to meet their tests and challenges inc. karmic ones - timid and cowardly, although going through would make them stronger.

Afraid to metaphorically jump off the cliff.

Stammering and enormous anxiety.

Fear and reticence about expression on a physical level.

One of the best anxiety remedies we have proved.

Helps us feel calm and courageous.

AVOIDANCE

Procrastination and indecision.

Snowdrop

Unwillingness to fulfill life's purpose, lessons of incarnation.

Those who sleep to avoid life.

Inability to embrace life.

Lack of motivation.

Desire to hide. Those who hide from selves, life and God.

Weakness of will.

Weakness and lack of self.

Opens the eyes to what you should be doing.

Dissolves false structures created as means of avoidance - so can bring what seems like chaos.

DEPENDENCY

Dependent on others from fear of independence, fear of breakdown, fear of being lost.

Great need of company, look to those around them for structure and direction.

For someone who is unclear, unsure, indecisive, do not know their own heart or will.

RELEASE FROM THE PAST

Brings freedom from outmoded structures of past.

Gives ability to see things from a different angle, to see patterns.

For those stuck in old patterns.

For those stuck in bad health or bad fortune and blame their inability to move on that.

Helps cut ties that hold people back.

CHILDREN

Children of parents who've taken recreational drugs.

For children who are fundamentally strong in heart but have been damaged.

Effects of surgery or vaccination on young children.

NERVOUS SYSTEM

Affinity with brain and nervous system.

Of great use in a culture where nervous system so under pressure.

Affects neurotransmitters and chemistry of brain - balances.

Heals nervous disorders, muscle spasms.

All nervous complaints - great agitation and unrest.

Metallic in relation to nerves and other rx.

Menieres.

Going out through top of head.

Mundane thoughts. Disjointed, forgetful, mistakes in writing names.

EMOTIONAL

Lack of heart. Selfishness and violence.

Helps both sexes integrate the feminine principle.

Releases power and helps in understanding how it should be used with the wisdom of the heart.

Sense of fragmentation.

Dislike of self and others.

Ignorant and innocent, with no malice.

GENERAL

Weakness, inability to get over acute illness - tired and inactive - a refusal to get on with their lives.

Vaccine damage.

Very hungry.

PHYSICAL

Eyes: all aspects of vision: inability to fix the eyes; squint.

Heart: works well on any pathological symptoms of heart disease and can lower blood pressure very quickly - good in acute situation.

Female: period pains, low back pain.

Back: pain L back from shoulder down, pressure as if will split. Spasm and pulsation R back.

Skin: chilblains.

REMEDIES

Connection with Dolphin for the ovaries.

Connection with Sulphur and the Base Chakra, for Snowdrop can bring people back into Base.

Apple Tree which it follows well.

Like Thuja, there is a secret they don't want to reveal.

Staphysagria.

Very refined and follows Arsenicum well. Its action is close to Arsenicum but is far more refined and goes deeper into all levels of the being.

Like Pulsatilla but different; deeper and more refined in its energy.

PRESCRIBING NOTES

Dramatic effect used in high potency.

Use high potencies for bringing down high blood pressure rapidly. Constitutional prescribing will be needed to maintain it.

Thymus Gland

The Thymus Gland lies behind the sternum in the centre of the chest above the heart and in front of the aortic arch between the lungs. It has two lobes. It is at its largest relative to the size of the body at the age of two. Its largest size overall is at puberty. From puberty onwards it gradually atrophies and is replaced with fat and connective tissue, although it continues to function at a low level all through adulthood.

It is intimately connected with the immune system and with nerve functioning: without its secretions the body would be in a state of constant nerve stimulation as in Myasthenia Gravis. It is also part of the process of maturation and is now thought to trigger the physical changes of puberty. The functioning of the thymus is also affected by stress, especially in children, and its hormones are produced in inverse proportion to cortisone in the body. Even in adults there is a direct relationship between the functioning of the immune system and stress. There is little pathology that affects the thymus apart from tumors called thymoma which are rare. The gland can become enlarged, however, which can impede the flow of blood to the heart and the brain. Conventional treatment is usually surgery. It can be damaged in childhood by accident and physical trauma, by fevers with opisthotonos and by drugs such as antibiotics and steroids which can cause it to shrink. It can also be damaged by severe emotional trauma particularly if this is sustained, such as continued abuse. However the biggest onslaught on the Thymus Gland comes from vaccination.

Children with impaired thymus function look fragile and pale are prone to infections of the lungs, ears and throat and thread worms. They may have evident blue veins especially across the bridge of the nose. Both adults and children find it hard to be independent.

Esoterically, the energy matrix associated with this gland, the Thymus Chakra, is an aspect of the Heart Chakra. Channellings from a variety of sources have confirmed that this is a Chakra which is currently being developed especially amongst children. This Chakra holds our karmic blueprint, the pattern for our life's work. Our identity, our deepest sense of self, comes from here. It also holds some of our deepest fear and pain and some of our worst karma - the stuff we have to work through and release or transmute. The effect of vaccination on this chakra is to prevent us from accessing our blueprint, locking us out of experiencing our true identity which involves our connection with God. It also prevents us from releasing our karma although we still function as a consequence of it. Many of the children damaged by vaccination and suffering from autistic symptoms are

Thymus Gland

locked out of their Heart and Thymus Chakras and forced to live out of their heads. For everyone without access to Heart energy there is fear and hatred which produces anger and violence. They don't know who they really are or what they are here to do.

This is a remedy which has proved invaluable in practice for the treatment of children and for immunity-related conditions. The notes here relate only to the meditative proving of Thymus Gland which was blind. The remedy was proved in a 200c potency.

ESOTERIC

Connects with ancient religions such Celts and Druids, going back into the ancient wisdom and enabling the soul in this life to connect again with these ancient patterns.

Link with kidneys and ancestral karma. Will help to clear quickly.

Can bring a very protected space, especially to a spirit torn asunder, not centred, the aura jagged and vulnerable on all levels.

For those who have negative entities attached to them although they are not conscious of it.

Will profoundly help those damaged by innoculation, radiation and those with dark spells within their psyche. Will help to exorcise these forces of darkness.

Connected to Atlantis and death by drowning.

Can remove much bitterness, hatred and resentment from the soul.

CHAKRAS

Linked with the Base, Heart and Throat Chakras - the expression of the love of the heart.

Profound effect on the Brow. Helps to create a feeling of togetherness, of each feeling part of the whole and the Brow is involved in this.

Will open the Heart Centre.

Will help gratitude return to people's hearts.

Reinforcing the spiritual contact with God through the heart and keeping our hearts open.

Promotes communication between Head and Heart.

Opens up the Heart in the Mind. Stops the intellect trying to rush things.

BROTHERHOOD

It creates a very strong feeling of brotherhood.

It can restore a sense of belonging to the human race and can re-establish brotherhood.

It can re-establish communication and harmony between people.

Where there are conflicts between people the remedy could be used in a magical way, affecting places or infusing objects with its energy.

It is connected with our guilt and collective responsibility.

For the pain that is the individual's and at the same time that of the race or humanity as a whole. The pain of everything that has been forgotten and suppressed which we all share, although we each think the pain is our own.

This remedy will help release something in one person which is like releasing for humanity. The energy spreads out like a drop of water causing radiating ripples in a pool.

Has a connection with ancient brotherhoods. Removes karma that has been acquired through brotherhoods in the past, like monasteries. This it can remove with ease but remedy bears repetition.

It takes people out of their selfish state of being locked away and enables people to be altruistic and giving.

Will enable us to see the light in another person. It will help us see that, no matter who they are or how they behave, they are a light being.

FROM DARKNESS INTO LIGHT

Takes us from darkness to light, into the light at the centre of the cave which is in all of us.

It brings in light; pure, pure light into the darkness, the dark chasms.

Is good for those individuals who only see negativity in others, who chunter on negative things, and especially those who feel sorry for themselves all the time, who can only live in the darkness. Will show the way and the light and bring back the joy of life, open them to God, their light and mission.

Fights the darkness within as well as darkness without and is good to take when you are confronting darkness or any negative vibration, for it will keep you surrounded in much healing and offers you a sword of protection.

Brings the realisation that the darkness within is our own delusion and the entities we see in that underworld are our own thought forms and those of humanity.

It drags up so much from the subconscious, things which have been dormant.

In very high potencies will help to ward off the darkness in the huge battle between darkness and light taking place on the planet.

It brings truths out into the light.

Enlightenment.

Makes you see and understand on a much deeper level.

It is a remedy strongly related to vision and seeing things as they really are.

Frees light coming through the eyes and light shining out of the eyes from the soul into the world.

Helps us to face ourselves.

Brings freedom, renewed courage, affirmation and purity to be used in the service of all.

HEALING OF THE EARTH

Within its energy lies a spiritual ether which comes not only through physical mother but also from Mother Earth.

Mother Earth cries out to be helped. Much healing must be done on Earth's energies and clearing negative vibrations. Many planetary vibrations at present cause much dis-ease. This remedy will help you to see.

Helps people to maintain conscious contact with God through nature.

Makes people more aware of nature and thankful.

Bring a greater awareness of the subtle energy which surrounds and pervades all life forms on our planet.

Remedy of great reverence for anything that constitutes life.

It will restore our ability to take decisions, to sense things while being in communion with nature, rather than coming from the intellect.

To combat the artificial world of concrete and plastic in which we live. Sprinkle the remedy anywhere in our cities.

Remedy is an important help in keeping strong in the face of aggressive biotechnology and commercial imperialism.

It is to do with the crushing of humanity and the Earth by humanity.

For those vulnerable to conflict that has arisen out of materialism.

GENTLENESS

Gentleness and equal steeliness.

The image of this remedy is light and ethereal but deeply penetrating like soft rain and has a strong affinity with water.

Brings gentleness and softness to return a soul to its centre, its spirit, its sense of peace.

It comes on the rays of the gentlest pink and blue, sparkling, radiant, full of life but so soft and gentle.

Brings such gentleness and softness, a real holding and supporting for those who are in need of it.

Comes with grace and simplicity. It gently sinks though the psyche bringing peace.

Sweeps through the subconscious like a surgical instrument of great precision.

Brings one-pointedness and clarity.

FREEDOM & RELEASE FROM BURDENS

It brings enormous freedom, relief and release from burdens.

Gives courage and strength to carry our chosen burdens in love and service.

Link to joy. This remedy can bring joy back when there have been heavy burdens.

A very powerful remedy to bring a person back to stillness, centre and inner warmth and joy. Once this is restored fear will just vanish.

For those who feel alone with the stresses and strains of their lives.

Sleeping to avoid grief, sadness, hurt and loneliness.

Helps where all the senses have been crushed.

SADNESS

Sadness about the state of this country and the world in general.

Darkness and heaviness. Sadness.

For those who carry the emotional burden of others.

As if weighted at the feet and powerless to move.

A deep sense of abandonment.

Thymus Gland

FEAR

Enormous fears which are difficult to describe because of their enormity.

For people who have screaming nightmares.

As if they haven't used the talents they've been given, as if they have wasted their life, producing a deep fear.

Anxiety, as if had done something should not have done.

FRUSTRATION

Frustration, not getting anywhere, not achieving anything, hopelessness or helplessness, like working your socks off and getting nowhere.

Utter frustration and helplessness about what is going on in the world.

WORKAHOLICS

Those who are racing but don't know where they are going. Those who cannot rest or listen to those around them.

For people who cannot be stilled for stillness brings great fear of being.

It is needed by adults and children who are driven, workaholics, those who use striving ambition to avoid their inner hurt.

SEXUALITY

Good also for all forms of homosexuality for whatever reason.

It can balance the adrenal chemistry and the adverse chemistry at work in the Thymus Centre which is the real cause of this syphilitic problem, brought about by those forces within us which serve to destroy humanity. This remedy's power can dispel these forces and bring in God's light. In these cases the remedy needs much repetition over a period of many months.

Profound effect on sexual immaturity and in those who do not mature correctly. Will enhance this process in the chemistry and heal the individual.

TOUCH

Strong connections with touch. There is a need to touch, also better for touch.

Remedy can heighten someone's tactile qualities and makes them more sensitive in the hands or fingers.

Can heighten the ability to use touch for healing and be more receptive to healing through touch.

GENERAL

Can deal with many types of schizophrenia from whatever cause.

May be an alternative to Prozac for people who are depressed and stuck in their brains.

It is of enormous spiritual value to children now being born, especially those who have been vaccinated or who are spiritually cut off.

It has strong effect on the will of the individual and will bring this to the surface.

Sensation of being crushed.

Physical parasitical conditions.

Where all five senses are compromised.

Stroke victims. Parkinson's Disease. Traumatic injury.

Poor co-ordination and dyslexia.

PHYSICAL

Brain: all the things that cause brain damage can be indications for this remedy.

Brain damage or parts of the brain malfunctioning.

As if the meninges are heavy, contracted.

Head & shoulders: pain spread around up into the ear.

Tension around the shoulders and neck.

Tension in the neck and the back of head.

Eyes: improves the optical mechanism of vision.

Breathing: cannot take full lungfuls of air. Diaphragm is tight.

Heart: physical pain and heaviness in the heart.

Heart and circulation, stagnation.

Circulation. Cleaning, clarifying the blood.

Stomach: nausea.

Abdomen: liver and spleen feel constricted.

Stabbing pains in the rectum.

Nervous system: brings vitality, healing and balance to all the nerve paths in the body.

Bell's palsy. Stomach problems connected with the vagus nerve.

Extremities: aching pains in the L arm and L hand.

Spine: extremely uncomfortable feeling at base of spine, quite painful.

Thymus Gland

MIASMS

Patients never present with the picture of this remedy. It is deeply hidden because of its syphilitic nature.

REMEDIES

It will enhance all syphilitic and radiation remedies and purify from the source.

Strong affinity with Red Chestnut.

Link with Cherry and St John's Wort (Hypericum).

Connected to Magnetite. Combination of Plutonium+Magnetite+ Thymus Gland.

PRESCRIBING NOTES

It is an almost universal remedy and has an astonishingly wide and deep sphere of action.

A good remedy for those who are healers.

Can be given to everyone. It cannot be overused. In fact, it is and has been very underused.

It needs to be used now.

It cleans and purifies the blueprint and brings to our attention our own blocks to cure.

It works in a very gentle and subtle but extremely powerful way and its power cannot be avoided.

A gentle remedy which causes little aggravation as it works. You watch the individual becoming lighter and lighter as they find themselves. They change from withered or gross individuals into refined beings of light.

It bears frequent repetition and its gentleness means it can be used with children and tiny babies.

We suggest now this remedy may be used in much higher potencies than before suggested.

Wych Elm Ulmus glabra

This is the only species of the wide Elm family which has not been entirely wiped out in Britain by Dutch Elm Disease, which it has managed to resist to some extent, so large specimens may still be seen. Alongside the Ash, this is the tallest native tree, growing up to 40m high and living for up to 500 years. It used to be common in hedgerows and damp woodlands in north and west Britain and in Ireland. It often branches near the base, forming a dome-shaped crown. The bark is grey with many long fissures. Unlike other elms which are infertile and only reproduce by suckering, the Wych Elm does not sucker and reproduces only by seed. This makes it very different indeed from the English Elm, which used to spread across the landscape in a distinctive lattice work, linked together through the root system. The Wych Elm is by comparison a solitary tree, disconnected from its fellows. The timber does not decay in water and was once used to make underground water pipes and milk churns and is still used for groynes and harbour works. It was also used for coffins, furniture, cow sheds and mangers and the hubs of wheels. Wych Elm has an association with two scarce insects: the White-letter Hairstreak Butterfly and the Clouded Magpie Moth, the caterpillars of which feed on the leaves. Grass and plants will grow under an Elm, unlike many large trees.

There has been a long association between Elms and the Elven kingdom and with death, the grave and rebirth. Different parts of the tree have been used for cleansing the skin and making soap and for treating leprosy, ringworm, sepsis and wounds. The tree is said to have a crown of light and to provide a link between heaven and earth.

ESOTERIC

Symbolises the Tree of Knowledge of Good and Evil because it touches both strongly.

The challenge of the remedy is to go to the highest level but stay grounded.

It represents cycles of highs and lows, degeneration and regeneration. Light and darkness.

It represents destruction before creation, the taking of energy, knowledge and wisdom underground where it remains hidden and dormant until it rises again.

Wych Elm

CHAKRAS

Joining of the Base and Crown Chakras.

Remedy for learning Base Chakra lessons, because each lesson learned is a kind of birth into the next level.

Particular impact on the Solar Plexus, on the will, stimulating it to move to the Heart and beyond.

OVERCOMING DARKNESS

It has great power and strength to overcome negative forces.

It has chosen for its evolution to allow dark forces to destroy its stream of life, its central energy. Its centre, will, solar plexus energy has been invaded by lower dark forces that have stopped the sap rising and cut it off from heaven. It hasn't died, but has fought the evil powers, trying to regain its life in a new way. Because it has touched so much darkness, it has much experience to fight the powers of evil and still come back to life. It holds lots of secrets and magic which we are not ready to receive.

The negative energy attracted by this remedy is calculated and cunning. A darkness that has knowledge, seeing and intellect but takes negative intellect into the heart.

The remedy will help deep rooted darkness within the soul that other remedies can't touch.

Can be used during exorcisms and the clearing of dark places. Can be sprayed around a room when dark forces are present. Can purify and cleanse much debris from auric field.

Never been well since any psychic attack - scar left in aura - vast field of action.

Very good remedy to give in all sorts of satanic possession and would show if someone was really possessed.

Can strengthen the auric and etheric bodies where there is a danger of negative entities entering.

TRANSITION

Transitional states: at the beginning of the process.

Those who feel too vulnerable when the light starts to waken in them and so they want to retreat from world.

For people stuck or relapsing.

Represents the negativity in all of us that is released as we get closer to the light. Helps its transmutation.

BIRTH & DEATH

Helps with birth and death and for all the physical processes we call life.

For those dying, at end of life, who cannot let go: stuck between the polarities of Crown and Base, not able to release into the light, not able to sink back to matter.

Opens up the elderly to light within and prepares them for transition.

Helps to remove fears and anxieties over what and who are being left.

Gives protection during dying even though given years before.

Very good remedy to protect the dead.

For a mother carrying a dead foetus.

After attempted, unsuccessful abortion.

In pregnancy, as Caulophyllum tones up the mother, so this would be good to tone up the child, give it much inner strength.

LACK OF WILL & ENERGY

No willpower. Aspiration but no will at all. Can't be bothered. Not much desire. Dampened. Nothing matters. Weariness. Bogged down.

Powerlessness, pervading the bones and tissues. Can give you back sense of control of your own life.

People who cannot make decisions, so don't do anything.

Brings courage to fight through battles, obstacles on the path, great strength in adversity. Gives fortitude.

Helps motivation with resolutions and strength of will to persevere.

Joyless state, can do nothing about it. So sad and weary, almost too weary for tears.

Lack of concentration. Difficulty making mind work and pulling threads together.

Burning candle at both ends so exhausted.

For people who tend to rush into things without thinking, going from one job to the next without stopping and thinking, which causes extreme exhaustion.

TRAUMA

Linked with disasters, physical injury, accidents. Can bring physical and etheric mending to a broken body, a broken aura. Where the survival instinct is very strong.

Those worn down by strife and whatever they do, they get knocked down, so they feel it's not worth it.

Wych Elm

Revives the spirit where everything is lost, destroyed and there is darkness.

Good balm for hurt minds, souls and spirits on every level. Works on transition processes, restores faith in the journey.

Creates a safe haven after a storm.

Space and protection round battered soul; someone who has been through a lot.

Overwork - strain of trying to run home, family and job. People who are trying to keep many things on the go. Can't settle, think, remember.

MENTAL ILLNESS

Mental illness, real psychosis, with self-destruct tendencies - attempted suicide, eating disorders, alcoholism.

Certain forms of madness. Where you get led astray into realms you then do not want to leave. You cannot chart your way through and become unable to struggle.

EMOTIONAL

People rotting away, e.g. in old people's homes. Feeling unwanted, uncared for. Lonely although in a group.

To make little people larger, sad people happier and dismal people brighter.

Want to cry, but can't or won't.

Helps those with deviant behaviour where there has been much damage to the karmic blueprint through vaccination. Can help the young, where the link between the soul and the auric body has been damaged by vaccination.

Stuck because of lack of forgiveness.

For those who feel split in two horizontally, cannot connect with heart.

People contained within their own environment, either frightened to expand beyond or no desire, for whatever reason. Lost faith in themselves.

Linked to bringing instincts, unconscious impulses into consciousness.

Scepticism.

For those who can only focus on material ends.

Teaches the art of discrimination, gentle and kind confrontation, questioning of our own and others' motives. Brings assertiveness, boundaries. Where too much is taken or given.

Wych Elm

GENERAL
Bridges between physical and etheric form. Integrates.

Has a powerful effect on all symptoms of ageing.

Lightens the vibration so much, clears stasis in the venous system, brings joy into the heart and takes it upwards.

Major remedy for those suffering from pollution, of air in particular, especially where this affects the nervous system.

For immune system breakdown as result of toxicity, HIV, drugs, vaccinations, VD.

Hunger.

Geopathic stress.

Asperger's Syndrome: no feelings.

Feeling of being small. For small men who are rather pompous.

PHYSICAL
Affinity with the head, nervous system, spinal nerves, endocrine system and glands.

Skin: rotting flesh: gangrene, frostbite, necrosing fasciitis. After-effects of radiation. Radiation burns.

Sexuality: unsure of, at puberty.

At the menopause and the male equivalent, feeling life is over.

CONNECTIONS
With the magic of the fairy world with its enticement, enchantment and seduction.

Elves and Elm bring enormous inner vision.

With crowd consciousness, a collective vision, crowd hysteria.

The colour black.

REMEDIES
Antidote is Chalice Well.

Lack of sensitivity like Phos-Ac.

Follows Berlin Wall. Like a spiritual Berlin Wall. Followed well by Rainbow.

Like Mistletoe, a good remedy to be given during winter, a time of inertia and hibernation.

Stramonium. Plutonium. White Marble.

Wych Elm

PRESCRIBING NOTES

Antidotes many remedies. Should not be near other remedies.

Works instantly.

Should be prescribed with caution for it is a very powerful remedy with many hidden aspects to it. Much has to be developed with this remedy. The light and intention of the prescriber must be strong when using it.

Crumbs from the Table

What follows is an edited form of channellings received during the meditations of two groups of homeopaths meeting during the 1990s. One of the members of the groups was a trance medium and almost all of this information was channelled through her from the combined energies of the guides of the participants in the group.

The material below is presented in the form of statements to make it easier to read. Much of it was originally given as answers to questions although some was presented as information we needed to know. It is written almost word for word as it was channelled, with the only editing being for context. It has been organised into themes as much as possible, but as will be apparent from the content, this is not always easy.

As with any channelled information it should be neither believed nor disbelieved but used as a guide and tested against one's own experience and understanding.

Homeopathy and Prescribing

Help for the Practitioner

§ You just do your best. Do not despair. You cannot heal the world in one go. Gently and patiently work in the background and your own seeds will grow and spread. Seeds of positivity are essential.

§ Trust yourselves more. You cannot be too wrong. Remedies given will all do something. Even if you blunder away in ignorance, as you sometimes do, something will happen.

§ We ask you not to allow patients to drain you so much. Keep your boundaries. Keep crystals in the room and after each patient leaves, surround their chair in white light. Use more magic. You can all use magic. After all, homeopathy is pure magic and it is only used in a positive way.

§ No remedy can do harm unless you are a harmful person and are using it for the black side. We do say beware of some homeopaths who may be infiltrating and do this but you will know.

§ Do not feel failures if people fall by the wayside. Many cannot cope with remedies at the moment. If their souls are ready, they will move with it. If not, they fall by the wayside. This is not your problem. Do your best. More difficulties come into your mind, we know. More questions, more fear, more "can I cope?" Yes you can. You have strength and you will be given more.

§ Not so much doom and gloom. Always try to make patients laugh during the session if possible.

§ I know you feel you know nothing. If that feeling ever goes away you have a problem.

§ Do not doubt or be afraid of your healing power. Treat patients only in the higher way of prescribing. Give them what their spirit needs and not what they are asking for on a physical level. This is the mark of a true healer.

§ Do not go so much by the books. They are history. Move on. You may not know what you are doing but do it anyway.

Case Management

§ If you see a colour is in someone's aura, it usually means they need it in potency.

§ Look at the four types of people and link remedies to the four types. Start on the lymphatic then the nervous and the other two later.

§ Every remedy has an essence and a picture, but prescribe on your intuition and listen to what the patient's spirit is telling you rather than what your mind is telling you.

§ Soul remedies will only work if the prescriber is working from the Heart Centre.

§ People who are not giving you information, in a complete state of subconsciousness, do not even realise they are here. Give them the appropriate miasmatic remedy and a picture will then form which you can follow. Carcinosin unlocks such miasms. Here is the only case where you can then prescribe it low perhaps three months later.

§ It is much better if the patient is not told the remedy. Many, we call them busybody patients, will want to know. If this is so, send them elsewhere to someone who will tell them. They are not on the path. It is better for the spirit not to know. Tell them later but not at the time. It means they do not want to move on properly. They are frightened.

§ When patients do not wish to continue treatment, it is the wish of their spirit and the fear of looking at change. It is not your problem although they may think it is. Give them what they need and let them be. Do not feel a failure. Their spirit may not be ready to change. The enlightened patient will see what you have to offer, even though they may not understand but they will continue.

§ If you are not sure what to give a patient, take a placebo and give it love. Then give it to the patient and see what happens. Only do this if you are unclear as to how to proceed. Only one is necessary.

§ You must be more forthright with your patients. Make them understand what you are doing. Try to attract those on your wavelength. For the rest, give them what they need and send them on their way. Try to observe the way the patient is and give them what they need. Patients are difficult, we know. A syphilitic task - which is why you are all doing it.

§ It is the choice of the spirit whether they wish to get better or not and you will not be given the power to interfere if this is their karma. Remedies are allowed to work wherever they are meant to. This happens a lot. The remedy can be lodged in parts of your spirit then will be stored there. When you are ready to move on it will be ready to work. May not be in this incarnation. Sometimes patients take a remedy and it may be relevant for their child, mother or ancestor and they may receive none of it. Therein lies a tale.

§ Prescribing must be changed now, people are so ill today.

§ Patients are in the habit of complaining too much.

§ The practitioner must be careful not to engage in power struggles with patients who are using Crown energy well. They won't give power readily for their own healing.

Remedy Combinations

§ Combination trilogy remedies are of great assistance, especially as you move into the New Age. There are many more of these trilogies you can intuit to bring back balance and harmony to your planet to enable intuition to be used correctly. Harmony is so essential.

§ It is important for combination remedies to be given in threes. This means a trilogy of old remedies.

§ When we say a trilogy, we mean a trilogy of remedies already in use. The new remedies, and increasingly, crystal remedies may be used to enhance the effect so these are not included in the trilogy.

§ Combination remedies for those who are balanced should include each of the three kingdoms: animal, vegetable and mineral. Otherwise give whatever is intuited.

§ Remember as you move on, more combinations, especially trilogy remedies will need to be used to assist the psyche to change, for a single remedy will often unbalance a being. This applies to both new and old remedies.

Old & New Remedies

§ Energies are changing. You all need to prescribe by using remedies on different levels, new and old integrated. This is required of you more now than before. Do not worry. Use your intuition even if you do not understand why you are prescribing so.

§ If you don't see a lot of reaction from people when you use the new remedies, it is probably because you give them with doubt. Give remedies with love and higher expectation and watch. Do not doubt. The new remedies are very powerful. If you doubt too much, give them with a constitutional remedy to begin with.

§ We say again, remember for the time being to use new remedies with old remedies which work in same sphere until the vibration has completely changed. This is why some of the new remedies when given according to very strong indications are not working.

§ It is very necessary to give the new remedies with your present polychrest remedies until we have made the complete vibrational move into Aquarius. This is a period of overlap and so for the time being, the remedies must be used together.

§ New remedies can be used for anybody but will work far deeper for those that are on the path.

§ The old remedies are becoming less useful. They do not seem to be working in the right way. It is not because you are doing it wrong. It is a time of change.

§ The information about remedies antidoting is relevant but becoming less so as we evolve. Sometimes remedies given in lower potencies do not antidote higher ones but beware of those that are inimical. The new remedies do not antidote in the same way as your present polychrest remedies. They work easier together and if you intuit to use them in combination, do so. Your healing ability will prevent antidoting. Don't worry in other words!

§ In all cases, rules are often made to be broken. Be forever open-minded. We learn too. Try and see. We all watch and learn from what you are doing. Have more faith and use these remedies more.

§ There are twelve trees, twelve stones, twelve notes, twelve colours that act as, so to speak, as constitutional new remedies. They are a core pantheon of remedies all associated together. And there are twelve star signs. How you use them creates the thirteenth aspect of each one. The most important is the essence of the thirteenth but it is always the hidden agenda. That which is hidden is often the key.

§ Remedy vibrations, as with new states of evolution, become more powerful as different areas of the mind and brain come into being and come into bloom.

Prescribing Strategies

§ There are so many remedies that can be used for cleansing. It gets very difficult to know which one to use or what combinations to use. At all times use your intuition and whichever remedy you intuit will work for it is your healing that works through the remedy, remember. Trust in that at all times.

§ It is very helpful to give certain remedies at certain astrological movements in people's charts. The planets have a profound influence and put patients through much trauma which they cannot resist, for it comes at the request of their soul.

§ A new system of astrological houses will soon be introduced for we have given this information to certain individuals on the planet and it will soon begin to filter through. You will then begin to see more clearly the harmony and interaction between yourselves and the planets.

§ Flower and gem remedies are gifts from heaven. They will not interfere with remedies. They complement beautifully and only work on enlightened patients. it is legitimate to prescribe on keynotes. Appropriate flower remedies in homeopathic potency can be given with other remedies and will not interfere. They work on a different vibration to remedies. They cleanse the intricate web of the aura. They infiltrate the atoms and do not aggravate. Californian remedies are not so good in this country because they do not come from here, also Australian. Our own flower remedies are more applicable to English people, they work better if they are grown here.

§ Hundreds of moles can disappear from the skin if the individual is ready to release and move forwards. These are disfigurements from the past. Each one is a wrong doing from the previous incarnation. Do not be judgemental though.

Potencies

§ Potentisation creates profound and new energy. It is an ethereal energy which is far more powerful than what is on this level but it also links into the past. It is pure magic and your magical powers increase the more you practise this magic.

§ If you are unsure that the remedy is potent and you cannot observe its aura, hold a remedy in your hand in an envelope and give the remedy a name yourself and it will work. Do not doubt while you perform this process. Machines are not necessary. You may use either paper or plastic envelopes.

§ The energies are better made by the good pharmacies or by yourselves. Machine remedies do work. The quality of the energy of the remedies is not quite as potent. They do work but the energy is different.

§ LMs are good. They will always hit the spirit even with the wrong remedy. If a remedy does not resonate with the patient the LM will touch them somewhere and go deep into their ancestry. The power of this potency is very proficient.

§ Always if going down in potency, be careful. Use an antidotal remedy in between e.g. between LMs and centesimals. LMs and high potencies can go beyond the aura so of no conscious usefulness for that person.

§ The effect of changing potency between the centesimal and LM scales depends very much on the individual patient. Sound and colour remedies will help here.

§ For the next few years [this was in 1995. Ed.] it is not so appropriate to use LMs. As individuals evolve and are less blocked LMs will be more useful to use. However, there are those with whom they will do well. Again, intuit these, but there are not many. May be useful with Oak.

§ Use more LMs but not if there is a block in the aura.

§ If a remedy is given high, it can go beyond the level of the aura and it never actually comes into usefulness for that person. It can be used by the ether or by anything else that takes it up. Remedies to be careful of giving in high potency (50M and upwards) to some people are Lachesis, Natrum Mur, Carcinosin, Thymus Gland above 10M, Baryta Carb and Calc Carb, Moschus and Tarentula. These are the main remedies.

§ The x potencies are refined. It is important that you should use these potencies more frequently, as they can open doors and enter in as it were. Also a 6x does not aggravate so much.

§ The prescribing of 10Ms of several large remedies within a very short time span, sometimes even one day, is wrong enlightenment. The process is too quick. It leans to allopathy and those prescribers who wish to do this should perhaps turn from homeopathy. Maybe some patients need this on one level but it will put them into shock and they will retreat to the Brow Chakra and not come back. However, some spirits do need to be shocked so maybe attracted by this. We do not advise this. The healing process should be done gently and slowly over a period of time so that the soul can progress. [This advice was in relation to old remedies. Ed.]

§ We just warn you not to prescribe a high potency for an aggravation. If you are unsure, a give a 12x or 6x in tissue salt remedies. These will work best. If you prescribe high on an aggravation, you cannot see a clear picture of what is happening.

§ There are three remedies to clear the picture; pick the one closest to the patient's constitution: Sepia, Psorinum or Sulphur. Leave these to work for one week and then look at the picture again. 200 or 200x would be best.

§ Under 3x, all energy remedies will soon fail, including colour remedies.

§ You can make plant remedies the same way as crystal remedies by placing them in sunlight or moonlight. It works well. In time, this way of making and proving remedies will be recognised. It is a New Age way of proving remedies but the old classical homeopaths will cringe at it.

Remedies

§ As Oak cannot be given to those who smoke or take drugs until a considerable amount of treatment has been given, if Rainbow preceded it, it would speed up the process.

§ Oak is one of the most important of the new remedies. It is like Psorinum or Sulphur and should be given first. It provides the groundwork for those to follow. Oak is a link with the Base Chakra and the first level of the aura and also the highest level of the aura. Oak is for those who are open-minded, those who are not stuck in any religious cult or bent, those who hear what you have to say, those who are striving towards the truth - there are many.

We say here the power of prayer and thought at the moment is very strong. Use these powers to help you to know who requires the remedy, but remember, not for those who smoke.

§ Chalcancite will act like Sulphur for the New Age.

§ Use Sulphur 30 then the indicated remedy 2 hours later where the indicated acute remedy does not work.

Give Sulphur or Psorinum every third or fourth remedy for people who prove every remedy or are oversensitive.

§ Always use Medorrhinum before Thuja.

§ Lactic Acid could be added to a liver cleanse recipe in order to release acid from the muscles at same time.

§ Hydrogen Peroxide would work better in potency than in physical form for detoxification. Hydrogen Peroxide+Clay+Thuja for detox especially of the solar plexus.

§ The energy of tree and crystal remedies does not interfere on any level with constitutional prescribing.

§ If Lycopodium is indicated but does not work, give Carcinosin or a radiation remedy first.

§ Use Chelidonium and Carduus 3x for draining with remedies for the Solar Plexus Chakra. This centre needs treating in people with phobias before constitutional prescribing will work.

§ Don't give Hydrogen to anyone who has had much drug treatment.

§ To clear the aura of someone who works with criminals on a daily basis: Thuja, Medorrhinum, Berlin Wall and many of the crystal remedies. Perhaps a piece of Moldavite to reflect the energy back.

§ Petroleum is a good remedy to give to politicians, to break down your political structure.

§ For treatment with cortisones: Berlin Wall, Stonehenge, Arsenicum 10M. Crystal remedies will complement.

§ Repeated doses of Syphilinum alternating with Phosphorus antidote laser treatment.

§ Ignatia is not used enough as a main remedy. Can be used just as much for men as for women. Useful for Lycopodium types who have trouble ejaculating.

§ Antidote to Plutonium: all sharps in middle octave repeated daily for 10 days. Calc Carb. One dose of Plutonium LM1.
Coffee enhances its effect.

§ Apricot 30 to open up the Third Eye Centre and to lighten the vibration.

§ Moldavite may be used like Mercury and Lachesis to get rid of patients you don't want. If they don't come from a point of truth, send them on their way. It would be good to use Moldavite to get people to see the truth about vaccinations. It is a struggle, we know. People are dense thinking and when damage is done they come to you for help and expect miracles. You again speak your truth. It must be their choice ultimately. Maybe give the remedy and leave them to make the choice.

§ Strawberry, Raspberry, Blackberry are cancer remedies, as are weeds. Best wait until the season to get the right vibration and then they may be made on a machine. Combine with weeds, use both together. Weeds can heal, especially diseases of a cancerous nature. Look how they grow. Sit in front of the plants and receive.

§ Silica is not doing what it should due to the amount of hormonal interference in your water supply. Pulsatilla must always precede Silica, even if Silica is indicated, then you will see the effect more.

§ Lachesis is one of the most dangerous remedies to graft upon an individual soul. It should never be given in descending potencies. The jealousy of the individual and their deception also become grafted on all individuals that the person is jealous of and creeps into their aura. The situation can become quite insidious because karmas become entangled. The only way to rid victims when you know the energy has got in is with repeated doses of Lachesis 200 and Moldavite in potency over months. This will deflect the energy back to the individual. It can also happen with Natrum Mur but here it can be cleared more quickly. Use repeated doses of Carcinosin Liver with Spectralite: it may shift it if the soul is willing. Grafting can be done with just one repetition.

§ Red and black butterfly if made into a remedy will complement Medorrhinum Americana and minimise and clear many of its aggravations. [Red Admiral? Ed.]

§ Give Carcinosin 50M for someone with no apparent symptoms yet who appears to lack joy.

§ Thyroidinum is very useful in adolescence and in old age for women but do not use during pregnancy. Use Thymus Gland for men and boys in the same way. The potency for Thymus and Thyroidinum should be 3x or 6x.

§ Cranberry very significant in potency to help with Crown Centre.

Conditions

AIDS

§ AIDS was brought onto the earth by the laws of karma to purify the earth, to purify souls so that the human race will again become pure in order to move forwards. Many will die, that is their choice. The sins of the fathers are being purified. The perverse sexual ways are being cleansed. This is a massive purification to bring us back to purity.

You can help very much with your remedies. That does not mean you have to save, but to enlighten the souls, the souls of those manifesting the illness and those 7-9 generations back who are stuck. The process is happening very quickly and this is a reality not a delusion. All is beginning now.

Addictions

§ Addiction is a very big question. It is syphilitic karma, a sycotic pattern. It goes deeply into the psyche and is riveted on the deepest level of the aura. These are very fixed patterns and the soul chooses this difficult karma in order again to transform. But often the soul does not realise the difficulty of this path at present and often they leave the incarnation without shifting it, for it is one of the most difficult things to clear in one life. Your remedies and especially your new remedies can help greatly but you have to peel away at the layers. You will only be allowed to do this in a safe way so that the soul can cope and it does take time.

§ It is even more deeply rooted when the physical body is coping and showing no signs of toxicity. In these cases there is often a possession, especially where the body appears to be coping and the entity within burns the toxins to enable the individual to carry on living and this needs to be addressed at some point. Use your intuition and peel away layers. Confront the entity. Let it know you know it is there and don't show fear. You have to be the one who is strong for the candidate who is encased is trapped. Again it is a karmic lesson but you can help.

§ Prayer is very important and keeping the individual in mind. These cases are difficult and more of these will show now.

Allopathic Drugs

§ Those on allopathic drugs have a weak aura with holes in it and therefore high potencies do not resonate with their energy. They go too high to do any good.

§ Patients on allopathic treatment do not respond readily to remedies because it is a process that has to be undergone. It must not be hurried. These earthly drugs are very damaging to the karma. They block karmic progression but it is the soul's choice. Advise and stand back but do not hurry any process of healing. It has to be done in a gentle manner. If you push a vehicle too hard it may not learn from the experience, which is why remedies should be left to their course. Let patients change slowly.

§ Drugs used in the past given as a remedy in potency should be used only as a last resort, because this can blow up the patient. It may be more necessary in patients who have been given radioactive isotopes. These are so harmful that the isotope needs to be given in potency before any remedy will work, but do it gently, a 30th per week, not too high, perhaps for 3 months, with the constitutional remedy working alongside so that you chip away at it.

§ The allopathic use of phenobarbitone has an effect on karma and ancestry. It calms the symptoms for a short while by suppressing them to the depth of the being, so the individual cannot address their karma. Therefore the personal and ancestral karma is put on hold and the individual becomes a walking dead person, alive but not alive and many heavy vibrations then stick to the aura. A negative karmic load, one could say.

§ The lesson about drugs will be learned very soon. It is beginning to happen. We have forces like secret agents working from the other side, infiltrating this evil and it is gradually breaking down. Souls have chosen to incarnate to prove these gross malfunctions and malpractises but it is their choice and therefore these people will learn and become enlightened.

Anorexia

§ This is from very syphilitic karma, many layers thick. It usually stems from a mixture of sycosis and tuberculosis combined on both sides of the genetic tree. Therefore it is very mutated and hard to shift as the soul quite likes being like it. They enjoy living in the darkness; you have to shift the consciousness of the soul, lighten the vibration. Often they need very high potencies and years of treatment. Those who need treatment will find you but often they become frightened of seeing the light.

Alzheimer's Disease

§ The soul has left. This is very syphilitic karma. The disease itself clears the karma and frees them. They are interesting spirits but people cannot handle them - we cannot. We try and try with remedies for this complaint but nothing will really bring them back because they are gone, so do not worry. They are not safe in that state.

Artificial Conception

§ We will say here that patients that have incarnated from medical experiments (i.e. test tube babies), the souls that are being put into these bodies are from lower levels and from the trapped planes. Consequently this can be a very dangerous practice. When they incarnate they can appear to be very angelic beings, but in fact they are from the devil. Beware here. Please. They will appear to be something they are not.

§ That is even more the case when the embryo has been frozen. This is disaster! We help and try and control this practice but many on your level at present have large degree of madness. It will be stopped soon for beings will be produced which come from the devil like this. Do not worry for forces will help them and destroy their negative energy for they are not a single soul but bits of debris from different levels. It is difficult to explain easily but sit and ask and see what you receive or observe the beings yourself and you will understand.

§ Children who have been conceived in a test tube are souls who have chosen this experience to help them progress. They are usually young souls who wish to progress very quickly for the incarnation will always be very difficult for them. They have little protection from God and often never contact God. Is difficult karma for them but remember it is their choice. You can learn a lot from treating these individuals but it will not be easy for you for the symptom picture is often hidden. They bring with them a very negative energy - it depends on when they incarnate and the energies they bring with them - but what you see is not what they are. They appear like aliens but not friendly aliens always, because of their lack of spiritual contact.

Cancer

§ Is a patient ever cured of cancer? The karmic seed lies within. This is no judgement; it is the choice of their spirit. The soul has chosen this cancerous journey in order to learn in this incarnation and therefore that is part of the journey this time. Usually once this is realised it will not return in the next life but in this life it is difficult to switch over paths.

§ Oak is for enlightenment and also for those who seek it. Prescribing Oak can stop the cancer entering the person's body and can shift much for them. Now remember if you can do this with your remedies, you are also moving very quickly into new awareness and enlightenment. You must not tell patients what you have done and it will only be made possible if the patient is ready for change.

§ If carcinoma is entering the aura and about to come in, there are no physical symptoms at this point. If you catch it on the way in and send it out again by whatever method you feel necessary, you have actually interfered with that person's karma in a positive way so as well as moving that person to a new state you yourself will also be given much enlightenment. It awakens things in you which are latent, links you in with the universal source of knowledge.

Cannabis

§ Let young people smoke as much Cannabis as they can and overdose themselves! This is the ultimate discouragement. Use your usual remedies to bring them back into the body, for this dangerous procedure will open the aura and if this process continues they will let something negative in. Yet sometimes the spirit needs to experience this journey for a while in order to learn. The remedy given in potency may be used but only in 30c.

§ When lower astral entities get close they try to throw you off course which is very much why those with drug experiences do not know themselves. They listen to lower astral forces and become confused as to what is theirs and what is not.

Children

§ Hyperactive children: Aconite very low antidotes adrenalin and is good for hyperactive children.

Hyperactive children with allergies from apples: it is the spray and the pollution not the apples. Treat them constitutionally, this will help to detoxify. There are no specifics.

§ Autistic children are lost in their own psyche. The spirits are usually those which have been trapped for many many years and suddenly incarnate by mistake as it were! Or often they are alien spirits who incarnate also. Therefore use your intuition to treat and gently work with them. These cases respond well to new remedies. Prescribe on the symptom picture but use your intuition also.

§ Dyslexia. The Brow chakra is turned inside out, due to second generation innoculation. Use Calc Carb, Thuja and Lycopodium repeatedly over long period to release the chakra gently.

§ Radiation treatment engrafts the sycotic miasm as well as the radioactive miasm onto children. Alternate radiation remedies with Medorrhinum.

§ Education. The effects of contemporary schooling on your patients are not so good but they can be overcome. The New Age has changed things like this and if left in God's hands all will be well. Allow children to be themselves, to follow their own path. Children are very different from you. They come in with a different energy. They are not as suppressed as you are. Listen to what their spirit is telling you. You can learn a lot from these little souls.

§ Retarded children are very close to God. Their souls are pure. Recognise that and you will learn much from them. They are difficult to handle but they are shining lights. You can learn much from them.

§ Asthma is often misdiagnosed and children do not have it. Pollution and inoculations are the cause of asthma, and here we say again please stop as many children as possible being inoculated.

§ Growth deficiency is karmic. Remedies which aid here: Thyroidinum, Thymus Gland, Carcinosin, Calc Carb, Baryta Carb,

Tuberculinum and in some cases Psorinum. Calendula will help the spirit and Bellis will help the spirit. These are of paramount importance.

§ Unvaccinated children are often more difficult to treat. They have no inhibitions for their karma is working and therefore they may be more difficult to handle but their spirits are free. It is more a problem for you as you have been vaccinated.

Crystals

§ If gems are potentised in a machine they can be enhanced or diminished in comparison to being made from the elixir level, depending on the quality of the gem. Many gems that are mined by blasting out of the earth will decrease in strength because they have given their aura a shock. Those that naturally come to the surface will increase. So if you pick up a gem and you realise it has a strong healing energy, assume it can be enhanced.

§ The best way to make a remedy from a crystal is to place the crystal on a stone or wooden slab. In the sunlight or in the moonlight, rain, shine or wind, it matters not. Cleanse the crystals first under running water for ten minutes. Place a phial of sac lac with the lid on an inch from the crystal so that it is within its aura. Surround them with your light and leave them for a minimum of one hour. This will impart the energy of the crystal on to the sac lac. There is no need really to give it a potency because the energy given from a crystal will resonate at whatever level the patient requires it. It will know where to go in other words. However, if you wish to use a potency, place a card under the phial of remedies stating the potency you require and then act in the same way.

§ There is a difference between crystal remedies made under sunlight and moonlight; keep them separate.

§ The crystal remedies will help a lot. They work in subtle ways. They do not interfere with the constitutional remedy. They enlighten, enliven, heal, protect, refine and help get rid of bad habits. This true of the highest potencies which will not get blasted out of the aura in people who are refined. In those patients with gross physical problems, those who have holes in their aura, who are completely physically depleted, you must stay low, but they are still of use.

§ All of the crystal remedies assist, particularly when you give a nosode.

§ It is good practice to use crystal elixirs in combinations.

§ Clear Quartz is a universal negative form remover in people.

§ Crystals work on the imagination and interpret states within the person, that is why you cannot quantitatively prove them. They are animated like creatures and have to be treated as such.

§ One way of looking at the connection between crystals and homeopathic remedies is that those remedies made by crystals go in an opposite but parallel direction to potentised homeopathic remedies. It is to do with the way time works or does not work and that many other lives, past, present and future exist now. It is why you can never receive on the nature of time and will never be able to.

§ Light is the most important way of erasing dormant memories in quartz crystal. The second is using a magnetic field.

Dying

§ A body should be left for three days - or slightly more if drugged - before burial or cremation.

§ The burning of bodies quickly in tropical climates has led to the entrapment of millions of souls, for the spirit has no time to be free from the physical body. Therefore souls continue to search for their physical body. It also causes souls to incarnate often and quickly.

§ Freezing does not interfere with the death process.

§ Embalming done too soon also puts the death process on hold. It confuses the picture.

§ There was a different purpose to the embalming of bodies in Ancient Egypt. Different materials were used, which were far more of a homeopathic and herbal nature and facilitated the freedom of the spirit - but that was only part of the process.

§ In 75% of incarnate souls the pancreas is the karmic memory of previous deaths. It is a deep substance within pancreas which will unfold within this New Age. In the other 25% it is another organ. Often a previous deaths blocks the healing process and is probably one of the biggest maintaining causes of ill health.

Epilepsy

§ This comes from mutated energies, and the destruction of part of the Brow Chakra and the closing down of the 3 middle layers of the aura. It is impossible to cure most patients on drugs. Try Calc Carb, Ignatia (the acute of Calc Carb), Belladonna and other epilepsy remedies.

Female

§ For release of aborted foetuses: Aconite 200 or 10M immediately before the operation, and Thymus Gland+Arsenicum Alb+Syphilinum 200x immediately after. Also Ignatia, Nat Mur, Syphilinum, Carcinosin and Walnut.

§ Give Arnica very high when women come off HRT or the Pill. Support ovaries after the Pill with Folliculinum, the nosodes, Medorrhinum & Thuja.

§ For heavy periods with no apparent cause: use specific ovary remedies, Folliculinum etc. Try a potency of the Pill itself. Also the pituitary needs supporting.

§ Morning sickness is always worse in tubercular patients due to the profound change in chemistry and syphilitic patients may be even worse. Often it is to do with the nature of the incoming soul. There is fear and objection to coming in, therefore they make their vehicle as uncomfortable as possible. This means that mentally and emotionally they do not enter with quietness and peace of mind. There are many variables.

Food

§ Many of you abuse your digestive systems. Please look carefully at what you eat for you all need to be strong for your work and this is well within your control. A little of what you fancy, not lot, does you good. Too much discipline causes a shut down of spleen energy. You must keep open-minded but have a sensible discipline within the regime is what we say.

§ Tea causes a marked stasis and laxity of all fibres, a venous stasis and general depletion in energy centres and in the aura. There is more but that is the key. It weakens digestion and greatly weakens kidney energy also.

§ It is the sycotic miasm also with syphilitic miasm that causes food to be eaten for comfort. Nonetheless it is difficult because this is a disease of the age. People do not have calm and peace within and therefore feel they can feed their spirits with the wrong food and this sets up a negative sycotic reaction.

§ You should drink according to your individual needs. The more you become in tune with your own body on every level and listen to what it requires, the more you will know what to take into the system. This applies not only to fluid, but to food also. Your systems are refining all the time.

§ All water is contaminated in some way but use your intuition which one is best and purify it yourselves. This will do. The power of prayer is very great, it will clear contaminated food and water.

§ Microwaves are a disaster, dangerous things, hold negative forces.

§ It is better to eat the fruit of your own country in season.

§ Nut allergies are very deep blocks and part of the individual has the will to die suddenly in these cases.

§ To enhance the clarity of the Crown Centre eat uncooked and clean food. Red meat is bad for spiritual enlightenment and so is fatty food. Lighter, uncontaminated food is better if you can get it and plenty of fresh water.

§ Some vitamin supplements can be very damaging and interfere with the chemistry of the body. At the moment it may be difficult to stop patients taking them because they feel they are better than drugs - which they are on one level. Take them for one week on and one week off so you can counteract any damage done in between but do not take them on a long term basis. They create confusion on a molecular level. The body chemistry and the thyroid are particularly affected, the systems confused. It is better to use one supplement at a time rather than multiples otherwise you cannot see the problem. Multivitamins should only be used for a short period. Potentised vitamins could work much more efficiently than the material dose.

Influenza

§ Flu epidemics are for purification purposes and the psyche of those souls who have these illnesses is open to receive them for purification. Much purification is needed on the planet at the moment as so many childhood illnesses are being suppressed so more of this type of purification is needed. December is the best time of year for purification.

Miasms

§ The petrochemical miasm causes much lethargy, toxicity in the blood and in the aura. It causes slowness of mind, dullness, stupidity, and leads on to much agitation and aggression. There is a big picture to this miasm. It does block many remedies from working as do all the miasms. It causes blocks in the aura and chakra energy. It is a heavy block. We do not yet have the most useful remedies for dispersing this. Those of most use at present are all heavy remedies.

§ The leprosy miasm stands between psora and tuberculosis.

§ Clear the radiation miasm and the heavy metal miasm, mainly with Plutonium and Plumbum.

ME

§ ME is distressing and has various degrees. It is complete physical and mental breakdown and the etheric body is shattered. It needs much repair over a long period of time. They need to be reborn in order to come back.

§ ME comes to those who have been shown the light but do not wish to listen and therefore they physically break down. This illness is given to them for a reason to make them listen. Some listen, most don't. If they listen they will come towards the light and move on. If they do not, theses souls can actually be destroyed. The medical profession can do them much harm. Luckily, at the moment, they do not know what to do with the illness, but the time will come. The soul is actually destroyed, can just disintegrate.

§ Remedies can help get them back to the light. The ultimate miasm is syphilitic, but there is also a tubercular content. Usually in ME the aura is obliterated, so it is better to start low. As you build them up, go higher. They have no protection. This explains why they can suddenly go down. They sponge off others and others' illnesses. They take on what is happening in their family group.

§ They are frightened of moving forwards and they have been given another chance. When they start to improve and then collapse, they again have not listened, so they need the same remedies again and some strong counselling. You can be very firm. More of this is needed with patients like this otherwise they will not shift and blame you for not shifting. You must be firm. If they do not like this they can go.

Menopause

§ Menopausal flushing is purifying. It is a purification from one state to another and these flushes purify auric energy and clear and cleanse the being enabling consciousness to awaken on wisdom levels. It is energy moving outwards and not pushed inwards. Usually if the flushes are too severe, the Third Eye, Solar Plexus and Heart Chakras need rebalancing before work is done on the Throat and Sacral Centres. Balance is necessary during this stage of life, for it is so important for the woman and for her partner and children. It is a process of great importance. So much understanding of other realms can occur if this process is allowed to happen naturally. Damage is done on your level by interference with hormones and you all receive this interference. We try to help. Your remedies can help greatly.

§ The pineal gland is greatly affected by this process, for it sits in the back of the Third Eye Centre. It is protected by the pituitary for the most part but once its energy has been damaged it can filter through to pineal energy. This why so many women suffer from insomnia of various kinds during the menopause and why so much fear comes in.

§ There are many reasons for women suffering from insomnia during the menopause. It is mainly due to not surrendering to this process of change and being fearful of it on one level. On another level, too many hormonal products in the system are ingested, not allowing the process to work as it should. Therefore there is the inability to switch off and surrender and heal. It is a complicated process and can be handled with remedies, hormonal remedies.

§ Plant-based progesterone has a suppressive effect during the menopause. More mental symptoms will occur - not in every case - but particularly in tubercular women who cannot tolerate the flushes which are so healing. It is far less damaging than HRT but still an interference with the process in hand, for it should be allowed to flow. Potentising this substance in this case will not be so suppressive.

§ The male also has a menopause but later in life, between 50-60 years of age. Their thymus activity must be observed. Prostate problems can be seen as part of menopausal problems. It is useful to use Thymus Gland as a drainage remedy for the prostate. In the male the pituitary and thymus work together. These problems do not respond readily to remedies we know, because it is a process that has to be undergone.

Organ Replacements

§ These create a block. Major organ replacement takes much karma and can become very diverse. The same is true with blood transfusions to a lesser degree but in a very much more subtle and insidious way. The same applies to babies who are wet nursed. There are degrees of this. On the light levels it may be necessary for the soul but on the deeper levels it is very detrimental. One could almost give every nosode to these patients.

§ When requiring a blood transfusion the patient is very sick and should not be given the blood of anyone else. Sometimes there is a fight between what is theirs and what is the donor's. Sometimes it is better not to give blood. Karma can be taken from you by someone you do not know and this will cause problems for future incarnations.

The same thing applies to sexual relationships with many partners. It goes on and on. These things can be treated through remedies and cleared so do not worry on your part, do your best. This is why some patients can be with you for a lifetime and one remedy will not touch them even if it's the one required.

§ Organ transplants are a syphilitic process. It may be repaying a karmic debt but karma becomes even more complicated if you take on the life forces in any form for another being. It can complicate the karma. It is not a good process. It is very possible for a child to appear clairvoyantly with the recipient of its organs. Use all the remedies for possession and healing. It is very difficult. There is interference in the karma again and breaks in the contact with God. To be used, the organs have to be taken before the soul has fully withdrawn, hence this complication. It is a very dangerous process. Prayer will help.

§ Remember blood carries the life-force, the imprint of your karma flows through the blood. The thymus holds the blueprint of karma but blood is its vehicle. The chemistry in the blood is important, for the correct balance of this chemistry gives you contact with God.

Parkinson's Disease

§ This has a syphilitic origin but these souls have a different quality. They really want to go but they are gone whilst in their body for years and years and years. They are there and they are here at the same time and play games with those around them. They are very negative and draw others into that negativity. Recreational drugs can cause that state but the ultimate cause is syphilis in the ancestry. That groundwork must be there. Some patients can be helped more than others, but you cannot usually arrest the disease. Again they are working through their karma. Some of the new remedies which we will bring in now can help very much to heal these conditions but only when you are told it is necessary. There are many diseases these days where people are partially here and partially not here.

Radiation

§ A combination of Plutonium, Caesium, Strontium & Rad Brom is recommended to act as miasmatic nosode for radiation. It would be advantageous to put this in the water supply and in the sea. [Helios have this combination, which includes other new remedies to enhance their effect. Ed.]

§ The best potency for the three radiation remedies is 30x, 30c up to 200 or whatever you intuit. The radiation remedies need to be spread around the planet. Put them in all water supplies and in the sea. The more you do this the more we help you.

§ There are positive and negative aspects to radiation as with all things. Radiation enhances alien activity and draws them closer.

§ The increase in radiation is also due to the activity of Pluto in the sky, so much more is being unearthed. More nuclear activity goes on at your level than meets the eye. We ask you all again and again to place radiation remedies in all water supplies and in the sea. One drop here and there goes along way.

§ Repeat radiation remedies every week for a while and then every 6 months for people who have had lots of X-rays.

§ The dangers of barium meals are mainly that the barium absorbs the doses of X-ray and every part of the tissue that this touches, the X-ray is absorbed. This gives the person a predisposition to cancer and if the predisposition is already there, it may, in a few years, cause mutation of the old cells. Certainly more than one dose of X-ray and Rad Brom will be required to undo this effect.
A combination of Rad Brom+Baryta Carb+Pyrogen 6x may give some protection but X-ray in potency also needs to be used.

Sexual Abuse

§ People who are sexually abused as children, whatever we do to help them, they take this through until they die. It is a very big shock to their system, it affects every level of their being. It is their choice, it is their karma and in most cases, it is because they have done a similar thing in a past life, or they have committed some sort of murder in a past life. In these cases, the higher levels of the remedies must be looked into. Certain remedies work better on these spheres than others and one of the most important remedies is Syphilinum.

§ There is more male abuse than you are aware of. Sexual abuse in males often results in homosexual tendencies in later life and this is where much of the corruption in your church lies.

Sexuality

§ It is important to balance out the sexuality of the patient. Use lots of Thymus Gland.

§ The difference in the sexes centres around the pituitary and the thymus or thyroid. This accounts for the apparent lack of development in boys compared with girls, since the male species is 2000 years behind that of the female evolutionarily. It is how it must be for now, at this stage of evolution.

Stroke

§ Stroke and paralysis is due to disturbance at the Brow Chakra. Try Calc Carb, Arnica.

Teeth

§ As amalgam fillings are unblocked, you will clear radiation from them. Radiation remedies need to be given 6 times, also Merc 30 after each one is done, then there will be no interference.

Twins

§ When one of a pair of twins dies, the twin that has passed over will always be on the other side with the one that is in incarnation and will therefore also receive the remedies. It depends upon the energy of the soul as to how you feel to prescribe. Usually you need LM potencies with these souls. On the other hand the lower potencies, the middle range do not work as well. Look at the vibration of the patient and feel which level will work best. These are very interesting cases and you will learn a lot from them. The dead twin may often become the guide.

Vaccination

§ Parents now are full of fear (about not vaccinating children) but it will change. The obstacle is really the drug companies. Light and love needs to be sent to them for they are working with lower forces. The root is money. These doctors will struggle. This is their own problem. Forces are about to change these things. Do not worry. It seems to be getting worse, but it will get better. People are questioning more and so do not worry.

§ In all cases, all children, are very damaged by vaccination. We state again that it must be discouraged as much as possible. Your coming generation are being destroyed with this dangerous practice by lower forces. It destroys their spirit and their contact with God.

§ The meningitis vaccine is disaster. It is so bad that souls have chosen to be born to die from the effects of this gross malpractice and then people will understand. Meningitis would not occur if it were not for other vaccines.

§ The MMR vaccination campaign demonstrates very evil forces at work. The vaccine affects many children whose karma is not always asking this. Make people as aware as you can. Be outspoken in your views, but we have it in hand. Support them after the trauma as much as possible. Whatever the symptom picture suggests, but the specific antidote usually works best given first.

§ Those who have been vaccinated and inoculated will never really be free. Will always have to work.

Esoteric

The Future

§ You are all aware that your energies and planetary energies are changing very fast. Almost too fast for you to understand sometimes and time appears on your level to be speeded up. This is a process which is happening and you must bear with it for now. We know it is hard. It is like being in the eye of the storm but you will be brought to a place of rest. We help as always. Do not fear.

§ There is much unfolding and your planetary energies are undergoing change. If suffering comes, it is at the request of each soul for their learning experience. Much can be avoided by groups sending out planetary healing and light into the darkness. Do not worry or fear, for the future may not be as traumatic as some forces would lead us to believe. Trust.

§ Along the next stage of the journey, beware of false prophets. Be discerning and listen within. Also remember, sometimes false or wrong information is necessary for you to believe for a while to move through a state of consciousness. Trust your intuition at all times.

§ Suffering will still be a large a part of the learning process at the beginning of the New Age. Many souls at present are much disturbed. Much damage has been done to the psyche. This will be healed. As well as your homeopathy, you must remember to pray, for the power of prayer and healing is needed and goes far.

§ The angels and guides on higher levels are coming down to help the world as a whole to change, to move into the New Age. The New Messiah is, as it were, a collective Messiah of beings from other worlds, other Universes, uniting to help this change. Many changes will have to be undergone on a personal and universal level. You must all move with these changes and be forever open to changes and also to be given information.

§ All energy structures have or are being broken down to move into new state of consciousness. The process has begun.

§ We are trying, and healers from other worlds are trying, to purify and give enlightenment and clean things up and this is happening and things are changing. The most difficult people to get through to are the clogged politicians. We despair, but this will change. Much work is going on from above to clean things up. Just be careful in the meantime. Do your best and keep taking the remedies.

§ All effects from modern day living will slowly now be phased out as we enter the New Age, the Age of Enlightenment of Spirituality. People must now look to their higher needs.

Chakras

§ There are seven major levels to the aura but within these seven there are seven again. seven times seven. These link with the seven archangels and the seven churches. It is important to read The Book of Revelation and the symbolism attached to these churches. The Brow Centre is connected to the Church of Philadelphia. Please read more about this. Each chakra also has seven layers and also seven crystals just to complicate things.

§ Open the Chakras and close them down again as often as possible. It will help your spine and awaken the kundalini which we are all working on. It is important that it rises gently and naturally. Do not be afraid, but love.

§ The Chakra underneath must be perfected before the one above can begin to unfold and work correctly.

§ Nothing will work unless the Heart Centre is open to unconditional love.

§ The Upper Heart Chakra is connected with the light behind the eyes.

Here is the connection with the mind in the heart, the third eye centre within the heart. It is a chakra in its own right and will evolve more as you move into Aquarian energy. It is a magnificent seed of light.

§ The seed atom of the heart is the place where the first spark enters through Heart Chakra at incarnation and the last spark leaves at death. The same process occurs. Sometimes during lives this spark becomes dampened and its energy does not work correctly, stopping the spirit entering and leaving correctly. It is a magical essence within Heart Centre. Sandalwood can heal this spark, at whatever stage of consciousness the soul is. This will allow the soul to leave through the Crown Chakra at death.

Cleansing and Exorcism

§ Crystals are what you have been given to cleanse. In every room you should have four: north south east and west. Whatever ones you intuit, but each room should contain them no matter how small. They still work. Cleansing them depends on the nature of the room. Perhaps weekly or monthly. Bedrooms probably weekly. They will cleanse and protect most rooms.

§ In certain places where evil forces lurk, crystals will not be sufficient. A ceremony of cleansing would then need to be done several times. Those related to the church who are supposed to be exorcists are, excuse my language, bloody useless. You have to be careful. These forces pretend to go and hide away. There has to be somebody able to see. At least three people are needed.

§ In some situations using an incense burner and a chalice for purification can be useful. In others it can be most detrimental as certain lower forces use these to increase their power. They are part of their ceremony of negative magic. Take them with you just in case and feel the ground as you go in. You would intuit. In certain cases physical phenomena occur when trying to exorcise these very low spirits. For example, objects fly around the room and shatter. If you are asked to deal with this, the key is no fear. The slightest bit of fear will affect these forces. Lavender is the best incense to burn for purification. You can also use a house plant spray or something with Rad Brom or X-ray in it. [Since then, many of the new remedies have been found to be excellent for exorcisms and for use as room sprays. Ed.]

§ It is most appropriate to wear a cross over thymus gland after any exorcism - will stop re-entry of any force of darkness.

§ Entities can hide within any centre. The blueprint lies in the Thymus and if you work with this Centre, you can often see where they hide but they can hide anywhere. Some schools are educating people to be aware there are no dark forces. Please don't listen to this for there are many. For with the uprising of the light and moving to Aquarius, the dark forces rise up also to fight.

§ Evil enters through the thymus.

§ Many of our patients bring with them lost souls and they can be released, whether or not you know they are there, they can be released. Often the remedy can release them or your healing power but it is part of their progression and karma if this is to happen. Lost souls are usually here for fulfillment of other people's karma - perhaps to teach someone else a lesson. There are other reasons but this is the main one. They are the cause of a block. If God does not want these people to move on, they won't. Nothing will work. Such patients may come to test you or those around them have sent them. They often do not come of their own accord.

Colours of the Aura

§ Overall red = syphilitic miasm. Concentrate on the Thymus Chakras here first of all.

§ Overall green = sycotic miasm. Concentrate on the Heart and Solar Plexus Chakras here, particularly adrenal energy.

§ Overall silvery blue = psoric miasm, the soil. Concentrate on the Base and Brow Chakras.

§ Overall brown with silvery flecks or muddy brown and grey = radiation miasm. Concentrate on the Thymus Gland and immune system and to an extent the Crown Chakra.

§ Overall murky blue = tubercular miasm.

§ Overall yellow and coffee = cancerous miasm.

General Advice

§ All the remedies that you have had in the past at this moment in time are working through every level of your being and are being taken back to your source and also to the souls who come from your source, because as you evolve they do too. The power of homeopathy goes so far beyond what any of you understand at the moment and you all know this in your heart. You are dealing with pure magic and as long as you are respectful of this, all will be well. God has allowed you to have this gift and you will all use it wisely.

§ The fear of power is due to your misuse of the power before and fear of the ego. Fear of the I. Remember the sign of the cross - the horizontal bar crosses out the I so there is no need to fear. Be open to your power and more understanding will be given.

§ There is much need to trust, love, surrender and remove the 'I', the ego. The more this can be done the quicker you will receive. The more you are still, the more you will understand and know, but this knowledge comes from the heart and not from the intellect. Heart centred knowledge is quiet which is why the more you know from this Centre the more you must be quiet.

§ We stress again the importance of working with unconditional love and humility.

§ Each night before you retire, sit for a few seconds and give healing and love to all and even your enemies and this power will help your intuition and you to have more restful sleep. Healing is like prayer - a thought wave.

§ As the positive energies around you push out, so there will become a disturbance of the negative energy on the other side. This will be stirred up and you will not like it. Bad luck! It has to happen. It will cause waves but do not worry. Be masters of your own body. Have faith and trust. Even if to begin with it is a bluff.

There is no need to search for a guru outside because it is within. In your search you will find who you need to give you enlightenment at that stage of your journey, for you are not alone on your journey.

§ Daily God presents to you what you need if you are an astute observer. God puts things in the right place also.

§ Face the fears. Allow them to be there. Do not fight with them. Accept them and they will go. It is not difficult. Be joyful in the state you are in now and you will move forwards more quickly. It is difficult to be in a body, but you have chosen it, remember, and you can handle the consequences.

§ In many of your lives there is trauma. You must be strong, have faith and surrender for all will be well. Do not sit in darkness. Trust and have faith. Crises come at the request of the soul and are important for the individual's growth.

§ Remember that you choose your life, your karma, in order to fulfil your soul's progression. Your soul learns and grows from each experience. If you do not learn, the experiences will be presented to you again later in a more difficult way. The closer you are to God, the more difficult the path, the more lonely the path, the more you will be tried and tested, but you will win.

§ In some cases, the soul is not evolved enough to understand in this incarnation, but it will give the essence of this experience to the spirit so that the same mistake is not made again in a future incarnation. The consciousness of some souls now will never be able to understand the lesson. God has not given them ability to do so.

§ We warn you to say little. You will be ridiculed and thwarted and damned and cursed, but you are right. Remain at peace within and we will help. Please remember you are all blessed with individual gifts from God. Remembering that that power is a stronger force for the good.

§ You must always keep grounded. It is no use having spiritual information if you cannot use it on your plane.

§ You must move. The word must be taken forward, made loud and strong. Those working in the light like you must make a stand, be seen, stand up. When you are lost the angels are there - make the connection.

§ Remember healthy living is important. Love and try to eliminate stress and worry. Everything is taken care of for you. There is no need to worry.

Miscellany

§ Left-handed individuals often have trouble incarnating and are not from this galaxy.

§ An initiation ceremony in Atlantean times involved a form of corrupt inoculation with Rose Quartz. Smallpox vaccination was a shadow memory of that and caused the syphilitic and sycotic miasms to coalesce like male and female.

§ More than half that walk on your plane at present have no contact with God, especially many who call themselves Christians. They are as far from God as the devil. Do not be fooled. They are full of ego and syphilis. Intuit who you can be open to.

§ Manifold effect, television. Good for keeping children quiet though! Don't sit too close to television because much radiation comes from the screen. The colour ones are the worst. Keep six feet away. There is also a type of Big Brother influence. You should be more careful of this. The damaging effect of television can be limited by putting a crystal on top of the set.

§ The origin of the Lord's Prayer is a vast question. It comes from God and is received by God, or that power flowing through you individually, if said with an open heart. It exists in all religions in some form and has great power whatever the individual belief or understanding which must be respected at all times. The Lord's Prayer in Latin has an energy with more power on dark and hidden forces. The meaning is the same but the energy from it is deeper.

The Brow Chakra and the Pituitary Gland

§ We cannot overstress the paramount importance of this Chakra. It is the entrance of all disease on the material level. It is the entrance and exit of the soul. Physically the pituitary gland is very small, but it is the most important gland of the body. It must be in balance.

§ The blueprint, the seat of karma lies here, the lessons you must go through, the sins of the fathers. These sins go back ten generations and the blueprint lies here in this little Centre.

§ It depends on the individual soul and all instances differ, but as a general rule, if the pituitary is damaged, karma can't play out its action. So if the learning process can't function, then karma ceases to be of any value, therefore the individual ceases to have an individual role. But many of these souls exist to help in lessons for other souls' karma. Their own karma is on hold but they have made this choice. These individuals do not usually present for treatment. Not usually, we add. Sometimes they do as tests for you!

§ Healing takes place in this Centre. If you were functioning in healing you would be healed and come back properly. Unfortunately this is not always the case. Love is of paramount importance in the healing of this Centre in yourselves.

§ Understanding is blocked if this Centre is blocked. There is a state of unconsciousness here. Most people have a problem with this Centre. The reason remedies often do not appear to work is because of the blocks in this Centre. The key to unlock this opens the person to their spirit. Some cannot handle this and are frightened. Fear is the keynote here.

§ Children live in this Centre for many years, listening, taking in and learning to control. Please note this Centre is damaged in most children who have been immunised.

§ All states of memory loss stem from the Brow Chakra, also all nervous disorders except hysteria.

§ Sleep is of paramount importance. This Chakra has to do with the sleep process, particularly the posterior pituitary gland. The spirit enters and leaves through this area into sleep and much astral travelling and healing goes on in your sleep. If the Centre is unclogged you come back without feeling depleted and this is the Centre that records dreams.

Try to get plenty of sleep. Do not go to sleep feeling angry. Do not eat a big meal for three hours before sleeping, otherwise sleep does not refresh, the spirit does not leave the body properly.

§ Pollution in the air damages this centre; additives and preservatives damage it; radiation from screens, television and microwaves damages it.

§ Refrain from eating sugars, cakes and chocolates and too many sweet things. Tea clogs the Centre also and too much alcohol obviously. Meat clogs the centre, particularly red meat but all meat does. Some fish clogs this centre, smoked fish definitely. Fresh fish would be OK but the oceans are contaminated so therefore it is the luck of the draw.

Wheat and gluten affect this area in the same way in certain individuals only. But many have this problem due to the treatment of wheat. What is right for one is wrong for another. Once you clear this centre in yourself then all will be made apparent. Use moderation in all things and be sensible. Be gentle on yourselves.

§ It is important to balance out the sexuality of the patient. This Chakra - the pituitary - and the Throat and Thymus Chakras work in absolute parallel. In the male the pituitary and thymus work more together, in the female the pituitary and thyroid. These centres are out of equilibrium during adolescence, pregnancy, lactation and menopause.

§ Remember the controller of this Centre has mastered themselves and the universe and will always remain humble. They will never use their gifts for monetary gain and never let their ego interfere. The meek are always the strongest. Do not be put off by those who are too intellectual. Your destiny lies within this Centre. As we have said, it is the blueprint.

§ Unclog this Centre and you will see. You will see the past, present and the future. You will see from whence you came and to where you are going and this seeing will make things clear. But in seeing you will have to keep quiet. Respect the gifts you are given and do not interfere.

If you are given the vision, use it to help. Do not use it to interfere. The two downfalls of this vision are ego and using it for monetary gain. We stress this again and again. If you abuse your gift, your vision it will be taken away from you. You use it for the good of others and not for yourselves.

The Posterior Pituitary

§ The posterior part of the pituitary is not developed properly at your stage of evolution but it has its uses. We give some important points on this part of the pituitary. Some of these points may hit upon the heart centre. Emotional release is needed in all of you and the need to cry and let things go.

§ The posterior pituitary has to do more with sycosis and the sycotic remedies work well here, particularly Medorrhinum and secondly Thuja.

§ This Centre is also ruled by the Moon and the Moon phases and has a pull on the cerebro-spinal fluid. Rhythm is important here.

§ The posterior lobe of the gland regulates the amount of water that passes through the kidney and the blood pressure. This can be an indication of the sycotic nature of the patient. Also bear in mind that this area brings forward the ancestral energy which is very much to do with the kidneys. The kidneys reflect the ancestral energy but the entrance is through this lobe of the pituitary and you can have a field day here with sycotic remedies!

§ The anterior pituitary is more concerned with Tubercular and Psoric problems.

Shock

§ This is the area of retreat. When you have been shocked in any way you retreat into this little hole of protection. It is like a cave within, a cave made of bone. You retreat here to protect your spirit from hurt, from upset and sometimes you stay here far too long and do not come back properly into your body.

§ Shock in any form damages this Centre often irretrievably. Many shocks to this centre within twelve months can predispose you to cancer. Again Calc Carb, Lachesis, Natrum Mur and Syphilinum are major remedies to deal with this shock and in children Tuberculinum followed by Calc Carb. Calc Carb often takes up the work of Tuberculinum; if it does not, this Centre is out of balance.

§ Shock can come from any quarter - from a loved one dying, from a broken soul contact, from abuse, particularly child abuse and or sexual abuse. You retreat to this point of unconsciousness because you cannot handle what has happened. The sexual spheres then become confused. The thyroid, thymus and generative centres go out of balance and you lose your Base chakra.

The Pituitary Cleft

§ Most importantly, the cleft between the two parts of the pituitary (and herein lies the main problem) is Syphilitic. If there is no link between the two, you are out of control and nothing functions.

§ The link between thought and action is broken here if the cleft between the two aspects of the Chakra is not working. You may speculate on remedies which would work on this. We give a few examples: Syphilinum is required first, obviously. And from this you will see no symptoms, no aggravations. It will work on the higher levels. You will feel that it is not necessary because it does not want you to see. And then perhaps Arsenicum, Manganum and Sulphur and use your intuition with the rest. There are many more but if you feel this cleft is broken firstly give Syphilinum.

§ We cannot over-stress maintaining causes. When damage is done physically, the psyche does endeavour to take over the job and refine the patient. It is possible but more difficult. For these cases remedies need to be given in higher potencies and repeated, some very frequently, e.g. weekly for a while, until you intuit the work is done.

§ The syphilitic manifestations in the cleft appear in patients who have a tendency to eat too many sweet things and chocolates. It is a marked and self-destructive trait and those forces come in who do not want the patient to get better.

§ Recreational drugs sever this cleft and it is irretrievable.

Remedies

§ Every remedy works through this Centre. It is the core of every level of the aura.

§ The remedies needed to unblock this Centre are mainly Calc Carb or Baryta Carb and most patients need these remedies on one level or another.

§ Carcinosin given here for pituitary imbalance in a 50M potency will bring the appropriate miasm to the surface within one week. This miasm which will be easy to see is the root that has to be treated in a patient. This can only be done if there are no physical symptoms.

§ Belladonna has a very profound effect on the Brow Chakra - it can blast it open in some patients to their advantage. Sometimes after acute violent illness this centre requires to be opened otherwise the vital force can turn in on itself and begin a course of cancer. Belladonna will prevent this from happening but it must only be given if the symptom picture agrees. It should be given more constitutionally but this tends not to be done. Deadly nightshade is a violet colour. Look more into the doctrine of signatures. God presents to you what you need if you are an astute observer. God puts things in the right place also.

The Power of Love

One of the great changes that is occurring with the dawning of the New Age is the opening of the Heart Centre and the emergence of divine energy. In the past, this awareness of Divine Love has been the almost exclusive prerogative of a few mystics, achieved after a lifetime of devotion and sacrifice. In the age to come we are assured that it will be known to all mankind.

In the meantime, however, we are in the throes of a period of transition, when the planet and its people are experiencing upheaval on every level, the inevitable consequence of the old order being broken down so that the new order can arise. It is bringing in a greater awareness of what is needed to heal the Earth and its people, as the mechanistic understanding of life gives way to a realisation of the importance of the invisible powers of the heart and the mind, of which homeopathy has, of course, always been aware.

This is a time of great excitement and joy and spiritual blossoming as we discover the power and joy of the Love within. It is also a time of suffering and fear for many, as negative forces destroy the physical structure of the planet, from the earth we stand on to the air we breathe, while modern medicine attacks our internal ecology and social and economic structures crumble.

It is important that those of us involved in homeopathy nurture the Light within ourselves so that we become more effective helpers to those floundering afraid in the dark and suffering in mind and body. To achieve this, we have to recognise the point from which all true healing comes: from the heart, from the deity within us, from Love.

What follows are the accounts from a group of twelve homeopaths of their experiences during a three hour meditation focussed on the Heart Chakra on 15th July 1994. The reports speak for themselves in their power and their clarity. They testify to the power of Love waiting to be released in us all through the opening of our hearts, a Love that brings contact with our true selves, knowledge of peace and joy and confirmation of our ability to truly heal.

"The earth is in great distress at this time and restless with the damage that has been caused her. Consider and become aware once more of the ancient religions, the Old Ways - the pre-Christian religions. You do not need to travel elsewhere, you do not need to go to the East. You are sitting on a great spiritual power here in England. Learn to re-awaken it and celebrate once more the rituals and traditions of the Old Ways. Be once more aware of the Green Giants, the Dragons and Woman. Those gods still do exist within the earth and are re-awakening once more.

The heart vibration of the colour Green is given you to remind you of your source of Love - that of the Earth and of Nature. It has been sorely abused and destroyed on the physical level, forcing its energies to withdraw increasingly from physical manifestation. We have not lost full contact with the earth energies, only physical contact has been lessened.

We need to restore the sacredness of the earth and her celebrations and rituals for two purposes. The first is to be able to contact her energies on an inner level and for this we need to go within ourselves, to raise our consciousness and communicate with the earth from our own depths. The second is to restore the old ways to help heal and resurrect the Earth so that her energies are available once more to all on the Earth.

The rise of illness and depletion - disease - comes from humans being deprived of life and energies which would naturally have fed and nurtured them. The dark onslaught of pollution, chemicals, unnatural and highly processed substances depletes and minimises the vibrations of humans. Mutation of natural substances is a dangerous process. In taking things apart and unbalancing the natural harmony of things, you allow evil intent and dark forces to prevail and have their subtle magic. So we ask you again to celebrate Life, Love and Nature. Learn how to love the Earth once more. Celebrate life with her because she gives you life. Learn and work with her pulse and vibration. Become one with her and you will become one with your Self and one with God.

We ask that you let your hearts respond and that you Love more and more. In giving out Love, you will receive more and your awareness will be heightened. Let your heart breathe. Let the Light and the Love be a constant flowing stream through your life and existence. The stronger they flow through you, the stronger your ability to give forth Light and Healing to those drawn to you. And as you increasingly allow your heart to open and express the Spirit of Love, like a stream flowing through its banks, the quality of Love will wear away your ego and humanity and bring you into the reality of your soul and spirit.

Let your humility and your compassion flow freely and in doing so you will take communion with the soul of others, enabling their channels to be opened and flooded with Love and self-healing. The Source is Love and Love is the Source - simplicity is truth.

In your art of homeopathy, your brothers need to work from the Heart Centre more. Some egos are yet strong and feel very threatened by your work and your approach. Give them Love - Love and Light will negate their dark forces. We send you Love, Love and Love.

It is fear that stops us Loving and Love that burns away our fear.

Without Love we are helpless, small and frail, alone and in the dark. In Love we are invincible, we cannot be hurt, damaged or killed. We realise who we truly are, the true Source of our Being. With Love, we know that our personality is but a temporary shell, our earthly existence but a brief spark in the infinity of Light and Love in which our eternal Spirit dwells. In Love is the only true detachment. Love in our hearts sets us free, brings us joy and lightness. By Love we are Blessed; with Love we Bless.

Love is eternal and infinite. We must keep our hearts open and radiate God's Love, emptying our cup so that it may be constantly refilled, giving and in so doing receiving, for all the Love we give comes back to us multiplied. From the Heart Centre we give praise to God, not for any expectation of reward, but because we can do nothing but praise. We express Love at this centre through Service.

If we prescribe from the Heart with Love, without fear and without desire, we cannot go wrong. How we prescribe then becomes irrelevant. Love is the greatest healer; through Love is everything healed and restored to wholeness. Anything is possible through Love without desire, Love without attachment, Love without an end in view.

The Heart is the bridge between the higher and the lower selves, where the Christ dwells between Heaven and Earth. It is a place of wholeness and completeness where giving and receiving are in balance, where a song of gratitude wings ever out to the Angels and where their Love is returned instantly. It is a place of non-judgement and acceptance of the present moment.

To see and feel with the heart is to know Love, to heal and let go of the past, to deeply connect with everything which lives and breathes. The Heart is the great forgiver and knowledge of the Truth is always welcome there. An open heart carries the healing waters of the Soul into the body and the world. An open heart can never be empty, there is enough Love for all.

The Heart must be open, honest, pure and clear. This Chakra cannot function or heal unless it is purified. Until it is completely empty of all falseness, power cannot flow through. It must be completely empty of false ego, be an open book, an empty page, pure and pristine. The six pointed star at this Centre is a diamond which has great power for good or bad, as it will amplify whatever is there. Therefore it is important to purify this Centre before working on it. The Heart Centre is about honesty, about opening your heart and revealing all. It is the centre of revelation - revelation of Yourself.

Love is the source of all things. It is in everything that has any energy. As Love is the source of all things, the existence of life proves the existence of Love and mere existence means that one is Loved. Love is indestructible.

Use the word 'love', for words have power in themselves. Live in the Now. Fear is the impediment that stops us knowing that we are Loved. It is this fear that leads to loneliness, a feeling of loss and being lost and a belief that in order to survive, all things that are perceived as threats must be destroyed. This leads to war, the destruction of others, self-destruction and a desire for darkness rather than the Light.

For a long time you have been aware of karma and the need to balance it. For many this has meant struggle and difficulty, a sort of 'working through'. It is time now to realise this need not be so. Reach inside and find the thread of love and having made contact with it, just pull it out. As you pull out this silver thread of pure love, it dissolves the anger, pain and hurt of the past leaving you cleansed and beautiful. There is no need to struggle through life, to struggle through old negative emotions and deeds. It is time for this great transformation to happen and by your Love you can create it.

Many souls are trapped in the lower levels of existence and need help to be rescued - brought up into the light. Now, as the earth's energies and vibrations are changing, it is possible for this to happen. Please remember and think of these souls - let the Love pour from you Heart Centres to them - this will aid their release. As you give to them, so you will receive. Your Love will help to reduce their fear and draw them into the light.

To be able to give Love, one must first be able to love oneself. Uplift your spirit. Give to others freely and see what you get back. Try it. As well as being an overwhelming emotion, Love involves respect, patience and constancy. Compare the rose to your chakra and its blooming with the opening of your heart. If you don't open your heart as the rose blooms and shows its beauty, no-one can see how beautiful you are and how beautiful the world is.

The Heart gives without expectation of reward. It is wisely generous in the perfection of Love's play. A joyful heart sings God's praises and brings the taste of pure Love which satisfies. The Heart is an innocent place where no evil dwells. Its warm light dilates this centre to become the dwelling place of the soul. The Heart brings us a sense of immortality and we see the Glory of God. It brings us to our goal of Peace on Earth. So be it."